European Technology

ROGER WILLIAMS

European Technology
The Politics of Collaboration

A HALSTED PRESS BOOK

JOHN WILEY & SONS
New York

Published in the U.S.A. by Halsted Press,
a Division of John Wiley & Sons, Inc. New York.

ISBN: 0 470-94755-1

Library of Congress Catalog Card No.: 73-9002

PRINTED IN GREAT BRITAIN
BY W & J MACKAY LIMITED, CHATHAM

Contents

PREFACE   ix

I. A BRITISH PERSPECTIVE

Schema: Collaboration and Cooperation   I
British Technology Policy and Administrative Machinery   5
Accountability: IRC and the Industry Bill   9
Philosophy and Objectives of Policy   13
The Advanced Technology Sectors   15
Conclusions   18

II. THE CONTEXT OF COLLABORATION

The 'Technology Gap'   21
Suggestions for Bridging the Gap   28
The Multinational Company   34

III. TECHNOLOGICAL COOPERATION AND THE
        EUROPEAN COMMUNITIES

The Crisis of Euratom   39
Technology in General   43
Industrial Policy   46
A British View   51
1972: the Commission's View and the Paris Summit   53

IV. THE COMMITMENT TO COLLABORATE

The Focus on Advanced Technology   57
The Aircraft Industry   59
The Space Field   70
The Nuclear Sector   78
The Case of Computers   88
Conclusion   92

V. THE PROCESS OF COLLABORATION

Questions of Organisation: Aviation   94
Questions of Organisation: Space and the Nuclear Sector   100

Equity and Efficiency   104

VI. THE CONTROL OF COLLABORATION

The Issue of Cost   115
The Concorde Programme   117
Other Aviation Projects, ELDO and ESRO   123
Withdrawal Provisions   127
The Parliamentary Dimension   130

VII. THE EVALUATION OF COLLABORATION

The Problem of Criteria   138
The Contribution to Integration   142

VIII. SOME LESSONS

Creating Commitment   152
The Scope and Nature of Collaboration   155
Accountability and the Public Interest   159
Evaluation and the Real Objectives of Collaboration   161
Some Unconventional Alternatives   164
Prospects for Britain and for Europe   167

NOTES   172

KEY TO ABBREVIATIONS   205

INDEX   207

TO MY PARENTS

Preface

The objectives of this book are very straightforward. I have sought to blend description with interpretation and analysis in trying to bring a measure of order where some will feel that, however desirable, order is conceptually impossible. I have for the most part resisted, I hope successfully, the temptation to prescribe. Like everyone else interested in this general subject area, I have certain opinions and biases, but detailed justification of opinions with respect to highly specific cases or subcases could not properly form part of a book in which the intention was to examine and set out what had happened and was happening, rather than what should happen. That is, I have tried not to be biased either in favour of or against European technological collaboration, but I am obviously prejudiced in favour of discussing it.

The origins of the book are threefold. First, it derives in part from some work on the political aspect of European nuclear questions which I undertook earlier with Professor Lewis Gunn. Second, it owes a good deal to the constructive criticism of the members of the European Seminar in the University of Manchester to whom I gave papers in December 1970 and December 1972. And third, it has been shaped by discussions with under- and post-graduate students, the political aspect of European science and technology forming one of the subject areas of a course which I teach in the Department of Government, Manchester University. But I owe other debts besides, not least to Dr Michael Gibbons and other members of the Department of Liberal Studies in Science, Manchester University, and to friends in the Manchester Business School.

I am particularly grateful to Professor Ghiţa Ionescu, Dr William Wallace and Mrs Helen Wallace, each of whom read the whole or part of various drafts, and to Mr Philip Gummett, who read the whole of the last two drafts. All the afore-mentioned and others, including Mr Keith Hayward, brought to my attention much which I would otherwise have been likely to have missed. Needless to say, I remain exclusively responsible for whatever errors have persisted.

I would like also to thank those many of the organisations and bodies mentioned in the text from whom I received assistance, my publishers for their encouragement and support throughout, Miss Marilyn Dunn, who assisted with the typing and, last but not least, my wife who bore the brunt of the typing and the associated tasks.

I A British Perspective

'Like it or not, we are going to create a sort of military industrial complex in Western Europe, which . . . will then turn into a space-age industrial complex, a high-technology industrial complex, a medical-research industrial complex.' [The *Economist*, 16 May 1970].

Schema: Collaboration and Cooperation

European cooperation in advanced technology is widely held to be highly desirable. It is, for example, an objective supported even by many who are, on more general grounds, opposed to Britain's membership of the European Communities. When one reflects on how much cooperation in this area has so far taken place the initial impression is that there has already been a surprising amount – nearly all of it, naturally, in the last decade.[1] A closer examination usually suggests that Europe's efforts have been patchy, piecemeal and subject to a number of more or less serious shortcomings. The conclusion normally drawn in the end is that the overall achievement has been rather indifferent and certainly inadequate. How does it happen that something judged so important by so many is yet so far from realisation? The answer clearly derives from the basic facts that European cooperation in advanced technology, whether thought of as a means or as an end, is an objective at the *European* level, while governments, necessarily the principle agents of such cooperation, are responsible, whatever their European pretensions, only to *national* electorates. There is a temptation in this situation to argue that, given an increasing degree of European political integration, European cooperation in advanced technology is inevitable, but that without it things cannot be much better than they presently are. The inverse argument also has its supporters: 'Paradoxically, such cooperation, if less *ad hoc*, if less improvised in the 1970s, could make "far reaching integration" seem unnecessary.'[2] Whichever view proves finally to be right, at this still early stage in the process of European cooperation, both are really rather sweeping.

This book constitutes a preliminary analysis of European technological cooperation, and it tries to draw some interim conclusions primarily, but not exclusively, from the British point of view. Since several major areas of science and technology are considered, and more than thirty cooperative initiatives, projects and programmes mentioned, reference to each of them is inevitably only illustrative, and is made without thought that a definitive interpretation is being put forward of any particular case. What is more, the cases themselves range from the purely scientific to the fully industrial; some are military, others commercial or quasi-commercial; some are project-orientated, others programme-orientated; some are governmental, others private or mixed. There is a sense in which the successes and failures of some of them are common knowledge, Concorde and the European Organisation for Nuclear Research (CERN) perhaps especially, but so far at least as the public record is concerned, few have been thoroughly studied and some have not been studied at all. In trying to summarise hypotheses one is faced therefore with more than the ordinarily difficult problem of generalising from a small number of dissimilar cases. Consequently, it would be remarkable if this book did not overemphasise certain problems and underemphasise or even fail to note certain others. It may also be felt that the book dwells too much on the difficulties and disappointments of cooperation. The justification for this is that the literature of exhortation is already long, that of analysis short. Furthermore, European technological cooperation, however worthwhile, *is* a taxing objective, and its cause is not well served by disputing this.

It is not unreasonable to ask at the outset whether one can in fact draw any valid conclusions from comparisons of such different technical projects and programmes as have been initiated on a cooperative basis in Europe. At one level, certainly, each is a case in its own right and is to be treated as such, and at much greater length than is possible in the present framework. But the search for broad generalisations can be justified in several ways, two of which seem of particular importance. One wants, for instance, to assess possible outcomes of existing and emerging cooperative options. And one also wants to be able to relate experience in the technical area to the broader political developments taking place in Western Europe.

This book will have more than justified itself if it prompts further consideration of these two issues.

Worldwide support of research and development (R & D) in the post-war period has helped to make developments in science and technology into major and continuing causes of political action. Technical change, it has come to be seen, brings both benefits and problems. In discussing European technological cooperation one is concerned really with but one aspect of the whole phenomenon, albeit an extremely important one both financially and politically for the nations of Western Europe. But it does not follow that in studying the highly specific political and administrative questions which arise in a consideration of European technological collaboration one need be unmindful of the whole in which such a discussion belongs. That whole, of course, includes such issues as population pressure, pollution and urban problems, primary and secondary arms races, technology's effect on the gap between the developed and the developing world, and the role of the individual in an age of headlong change. In particular, a preference for the retention of national units as independent as possible in a world which crushes independence is very defensible. That needs to be admitted here. Those who hold this position frequently point in the technological sector to the example of Sweden, arguing that what is seemingly possible for her should be even more feasible for Britain, perhaps forgetting that size may reduce rather than expand the availability of options. It is not the business of this book to explore fully that alternative. What is not conceded here is that a Europe technologically, industrially and politically strong is necessarily incompatible with a deep national and European concern for the control of technology and for its harnessing in pursuit of socially, as opposed to commercially or militarily, determined ends.

The book considers first the phenomenon of the 'technological gap', together with suggestions made for bridging it, and then briefly examines the efforts in the technological field of the European Communities, for which organisation cooperation could formally be viewed as much as a means to more general integration as an end in itself. The more important features of European technological collaboration outside the EEC are then assessed; these are cases where collaboration is more an end in itself. There seem in fact to be some grounds, if not very strong ones, for distinguishing on this basis between 'cooperation' and 'collaboration', and so far as possible these terms are retained in the remainder of the book. Cases of collaboration are dealt with under the headings of commitment, process, control and evaluation. These headings have been adopted as deriving more or less naturally from the experience of collaboration. The argument for having some set of organising concepts is that it is impossible otherwise to get the wide range of collaborative ventures into any kind of comparative perspective. The argument for this particular set is that it seems possible to summarise in its terms the major problems shaping and underlying any policy of collaboration. It is worth noting at this stage, and the point will be developed later, that as defined here the issues represented by these four headings contain both managerial or technocratic and democratic or, at least, political aspects.

By 'commitment' will be meant the context of the initiative to collaborate, the depth of the involvement and the circumstances of failure to collaborate. 'Process' is taken to refer to two connected questions: first come the organisational and procedural arrangements, whether formal or informal, employed to ensure that collaborative undertakings are properly conducted, as well in technical spirit as in political fact; second is the striking of an appropriate balance between efficiency, understood in the usual sense of an optimum ratio between output and input, and equity, the fair division of work between collaborating parties. 'Control' relates, naturally, to the monitoring of costs, but for present purposes is also taken to include withdrawal provisions and the role of parliamentary agencies in securing a wider accountability. 'Evaluation' is inevitably still more of a blanket concept, since it must subsume questions involving subjective and objective criteria and of the evolving political, technical and commercial environment of collaboration. And what connection should one expect or prescribe between evaluation of activities in the past and new commitments in the future? 'Provisional appraisal' might be a better heading for this section, in which an attempt is also made to relate the substantive content of collaborative and cooperative projects to matters of more general economic and political integration. It is here that one finds the analysis particularly unsatisfactory, for reasons, one would naturally like to believe, inherent in the subject matter. Certainly this book cannot pretend to offer a full interpretation of the relationship between technological collaboration and political or economic integration. Equally certainly, Europeans have not so far thought sufficiently deeply about this relationship and how they would wish it to develop.

British Technology Policy and Administrative Machinery

The juxtaposition of 'Europe' and 'technology' will bring to most minds the four so-called 'advanced technology sectors' of aviation, space, nuclear energy and computers. It may be useful both to summarise very briefly here the main characteristics of the policies followed by successive British Governments in these fields, and to put these summaries in some still broader context. There is to begin with a semantic difficulty. When one speaks of a policy for the nuclear industry one has in mind, for the most part, an essentially explicit set of provisions, guidelines and so on, which from time to time one may expect to see set out in, say, a White Paper or ministerial speech. But the idea of a 'technology policy' is considerably more general. It is not only the summation of such policies as that, or part of that, laid down for the nuclear industry, but in addition contains much less clear-cut factors and influences, and one does not look, and it is not easy to see that one should, for any kind of detailed statement of it from government. 'Technology policy' merges at one end into policies for science, and therefore also for education, and at the other into policies for transport, energy, industry and so on, and these are themselves part of economic policy more generally. There is also an important connection between 'technology policy' and defence. One is concerned here not to argue that government should, for instance, separately formulate a policy for technology or for R & D, but instead to emphasise the fact that this book is to some extent based on the necessary but artificial identification of technology, and even worse 'advanced' technology, as a policy area.[3]

It was in the decade after 1962 that British politicians really discovered both the political glamour and the economic pain of technology, especially of advanced or more accurately 'big' technology. The Labour Party's realisation in Opposition that Britain's difficulties in exploiting technical change were economically serious and therefore politically significant have been fully charted and there is no occasion to re-examine that ground here.[4] Of greater interest are the consequences which flowed from this appreciation during the years of the Labour Government from 1964–70. It makes some sense to divide these consequences into two very broad categories, those that bore on administrative structures and those that more directly affected policy. With similar simplification, it is helpful to recall two general circumstances relating to this period. First, with respect to policy towards technology and industry, there was substantial continuity between the views which the Conservative Government evolved in their last two years, 1962–64, and the views of the subsequent Labour Government, a continuity which in large measure has been re-established after a brief, but passionate and fascinating, flirtation by the Conservatives with a very different approach, immediately before and after the General Election of 1970. One might also note with regard to administrative structure that, due allowance being made for empiricism, there has been more common ground between the parties than might appear at first glance. And it is also not unimportant that the departmental changes at least seem for the most part to have enjoyed the support of the third party in the state, the civil service.[5] The other general feature of the 1962–70 period, the critical constraint in fact, was the doubtful general health of the British economy, and in particular the essential failure by 1966 of detailed economic planning.

With these factors, continuity of philosophy and persisting economic uncertainty, borne in mind, the basic characteristic of government policy towards industry and technology in the decade after 1962 can fairly be described as interventionism or, remembering the Conservative departure of 1970–71, a growing interventionism (1962–1970), an attempt to disengage (1970–71), and a return to interventionism (1971–   ). But what exactly does one mean by interventionism? Nothing less than the deliberate involvement of government or its agencies in the industrial sector, whether public or private, with conscious discrimination, financial or otherwise, being practised between industries, technologies, companies or managements or on the basis of geographical location. One is more concerned here with a political than an economic definition, but even so this is by no means a precise one. The last decade has also seen many more emotive descriptions: government no longer holding, but in, the 'ring'; a government of laws giving way to a government of men; the state the highly selective patron of its industrial society; the response of 'positive' government to the 'imperatives' of technology.[6]

And how has interventionism been prosecuted? To identify for convenience another dichotomy, first, by the promotion of industrial restructuring, and second, by the provision of financial and other assistance and inducements for somewhat less drastic objectives connected with efficiency, modernisation and innovation. This obvious simplification may be felt to exclude or underemphasise certain other interventionist techniques associated with 'planning', fiscal incentives, legal changes and so on, but it is a robust enough classification for the purposes of this introduction.[7] However, it is well to stress that by 1970 'intervention' had, especially for its critics, come to stand for a wide range of developments, including for instance the evolution of 'interventionist' ministries like the Ministry of Technology, the operations of quasi-governmental bodies like the Industrial Reorganisation Corporation (IRC) and the Shipbuilding Industry Board (SIB), the expanded role of others like the National Research Development Corporation (NRDC), the philosophy behind the Science and Technology Act of 1965 and the Industrial Expansion Act of 1968, specific projects like Concorde and the RB211, and, last but not least, investment allowances and regional assistance. It was the multiplicity and financial power of all these projects, schemes and incentives combined which, as the *Economist* put it, between 1964 and 1970 'established the government as a major industrial force'.[8]

A dichotomy having been suggested for explanatory purposes in the case of the policies of interventionism, it may for the same reason be useful to distinguish two sorts of administrative development associated with the implementation of these policies, namely the progressive reorganisation of government departments, in particular those responsible for industry and technology, and the creation of new, and the stimulation of old, quasi-governmental bodies. In the first category, easily the most striking development under the Labour Government was the rise of the Ministry of Technology, and under the Conservatives in 1970, its replacement by the Department of Trade and Industry (DTI).[9] Created in October 1964 to 'guide and stimulate a major national effort to bring advanced technology and new processes into British industry', the Ministry of Technology was initially given sponsorship functions, in the sense of being the main point of contact with the government machine, for four industries – computers, machine tools, electronics and telecommunications. Soon after, it assumed responsibility for the Atomic Energy Authority (AEA), the NRDC and most of the facilities of the former Department of Scientific and Industrial Research (DSIR). In due course the sponsorship function gradually extended to cover almost the whole of the electrical, electronic and mechanical engineering industries, motor vehicles, process plant, and shipbuilding. Other responsibilities were also added, for instance in the field of standards. At the end of 1966 the Ministry absorbed the Ministry of Aviation, a department several times its own size, acquiring thereby that department's major R & D facilities and sponsorship functions for airframes, aeroengines, avionics and aerospace generally, as well as major defence procurement responsibilities. Other smaller changes followed and then, in October 1969, the Ministry reached its apotheosis, absorbing completely the Ministry of Power and taking over, from the Board of Trade, responsibility for the chemical and textile industries and for industrial location, and, from the Department of Economic Affairs (DEA), sponsorship of the IRC. With the return of a Conservative Government in 1970 the Ministry was merged with the Board of Trade to form the Department of Trade and Industry, its aviation section being separated out to form the temporary Ministry of Aviation Supply, pending the formation, after a report by a working party, of a new Procurement Executive.

The most important general conclusions to be drawn from the steady expansion of this technological empire would seem to be: first and most obvious, that there has been a continuing search for the 'right', or at least for a 'better', organisation of government's relationships with industry and for a more effective arrangement of its own R & D facilities; but second and more fundamental, eventually reasserting itself even in the case of the DTI, acceptance of the extensive and essentially permanent nature of the new kinds of government-industry links created in the 1960s. Detailed analysis is still awaited of the philosophy, pressures and arbitrary events which shaped the Ministry of Technology's evolution and character, from the weakling of 1964, through the Ministry of Industry it effectively became in 1969, to the DTI of the new

Conservative years. One notes here only that the Ministry of Technology, already in 1967 'the biggest State-directed complex of scientific and industrial power in Europe', was even then, in the judgement of one political scientist, the department in which the doctrine of ministerial responsibility was 'stretched thinner . . . than perhaps anywhere else'.[10] 'A vast, amorphous jellyfish of a department . . . a veritable nightmare', Sir Keith Joseph, the Opposition spokesman on technology, called it in October 1969,[11] but the new DTI was hardly less of a Superministry, and there were soon to be severe criticisms of it too.

Accountability: IRC and the Industry Bill

Between 1962 and 1972 the context of government decision-making for industry and technology may have improved, because *inter alia* of better departmental organisation and the closer intermingling of administrative and technical civil servants, the latter especially encouraged by the Ministry of Technology and the DTI. And during the same period the criteria of decision-making may also have been strengthened, in the light of bitter experience as well as of theoretical study. Nevertheless, despite such developments as the Parliamentary Select Committee on Science and Technology, it does not seem either too uncharitable or too inaccurate to suggest that the true accountability of this decision-making has remained somewhat short of what it might profitably have been.

But if this stricture is justified in the case of direct departmental decision-making, and the matter is naturally open to debate, is it not necessarily even more true of the second important administrative development of the 1960s noted above, the proliferation, especially under the Labour Government, of quasi-governmental bodies ? These after all are by definition further removed than are departments from parliamentary scrutiny. Many of those created or amended after 1964 had a very important impact on industry generally, e.g. the National Board for Prices and Incomes (NBPI), or on a specific industry, e.g. the SIB, but none had greater overall significance for British industrial technology than did the IRC. Originally placed under the DEA but always closely associated with the Ministry of Technology, and eventually reporting to it, the IRC Board in fact enjoyed in their deliberations a remarkable amount of freedom from political interference by the formally responsible department, and also from the normal demands of parliamentary investigation, only once appearing before a parliamentary committee, and then on a specific issue rather than to account for the Corporation's general behaviour. Indeed, the Minister of Technology in his defence of the IRC concept argued that 'when you are talking of IRC you are not talking of the Government you are talking of a public merchant bank'.

No assessment of the IRC's activities can be made here but the matter of accountability needs briefly to be pursued.[12] The IRC was wound up by the Conservative Government in their Industry Act of 1971, which also terminated the previous Labour Government's Industrial Expansion Act (IEA), and the question of accountability is highlighted by comparing the debate on this Act of 1971 with that on the 1972 Act of the same name. During the first, the Secretary of State for Trade and Industry explained that so far as the Government were concerned, an 'essential objection' common to the IRC and the IEA was that they were selective and discriminating, but yet not subject to full parliamentary discipline. The Minister, Mr John Davies, can hardly have foreseen that in only a year he himself would find it necessary to recreate a formal instrument of discriminatory intervention, but he did add: 'It may well be that at some future date we shall be faced with a similar problem. When we are, we should submit ourselves to the full discipline of Parliament.' The Minister also made it clear that by Parliamentary discipline he meant approval before rather than after the event, and in the same regard a junior minister, Mr Nicholas Ridley, argued that although the IEA had been 'all right because it forced the Government to make an order in each case', the IRC Act had allowed that body to 'do as it wished'.[13]

The most controversial part of the 1972 Industry Bill lay in its middle section, which provided for 'selective financial assistance for industry in the development areas, the intermediate areas and Northern Ireland' and, 'subject to certain conditions and limitations, generally'. The assistance was to be made available to promote modernisation and efficiency, to encourage expansion or reconstruction, to ensure an appropriate distribution of plant and to permit orderly contraction in an industry. A sum of £250 millions was to be set aside for the purpose, together with two further sums of £150 millions on affirmative parliamentary resolution. Expenditure was expected to reach some £75 millions annually by the mid-seventies and the provision was to be terminated on 31 December 1977, at the end of the transition period of Britain's entry into Europe. The Government could proceed by offering guarantees, loans, grants, or by investment, but shares were to be obtained only with the consent of the company concerned, they were to be held for as little time as possible, and resort to the fund was in all cases to be conditional on there being no alternative source of finance. It had been announced in March 1972 that a Minister for Industrial Development was to be appointed, responsible to the Secretary of State for Trade and Industry, and head of an Industrial Development Executive, effectively a sub-department and itself containing a Development Unit capable of appraising and implementing industrial projects.[14]

The Confederation of British Industry (CBI) were initially much exercised by what they saw as the unfettered power given to the Minister by Clause 8 of the Bill, the organisation's president referring to the original provision as 'pernicious'. They wanted the criteria of assistance to be specified more exactly, real powers to be given to an Industrial Development Board, which would advise the Minister, and more accountability generally.[15] The Secretary of State explained later to the Commons that the difficulty lay in drafting criteria which amounted neither to an 'open door' nor on the other hand to too tight an impediment on action, but the CBI's reservations were met by putting the Industrial Development Advisory Board of bankers, industrialists and accountants on a statutory basis, by laying down that Parliament be informed if Board and Minister disagreed, by providing for an annual report and by putting narrower restrictions on the availability of the £550 millions allocated for selective assistance.[16]

The Labour Opposition, while objecting to certain aspects of the Industry Bill, naturally welcomed its general philosophy and savoured with delight the Government's discomfiture. Mr Wedgwood Benn reminded the Secretary of State that he had not 'invented socialist intervention in a mixed economy', and insisted of the Minister's Bill that, by comparison with Labour's measures which the Conservatives had wound up the previous year, 'The powers are wider, the amount of money is greater, the criteria are looser, the degree of accountability is less'.[17]

The Minister for Industrial Development, conceding that superficially one could 'make something of a go' of the argument that there was a parallel between the IEA and the new Industry Bill, nevertheless maintained that the essential difference lay in the matter of accountability or answerability:

> 'The argument for a State holding fund or for an IRC is that it will not be mucked about by politicians, that it will be allowed to get on with its job with a pristine commercial purity. The argument against that is that there will be less parliamentary accountability'.[18]

In accepting an amendment to the Bill so that projects costing in excess of £5 millions would require an affirmative parliamentary resolution, and in reducing the financial tranches from £250 millions and, on affirmative resolution two £150 millions sums, to £150 millions and four £100 millions sums, the Minister, Mr Chataway, claimed that this would ensure 'total parliamentary accountability' in a sense that had been lacking with the IRC. The same point was also stressed by the Secretary of State, who acknowledged that he was conscious of a 'heavy responsibility not least to justify to those who might be the victims of . . . discrimination the methods practised and the decisions reached'.[19]

In what is an extremely brief treatment of intervention it has seemed desirable for three reasons to focus on the 1972 Industry Act, and in connection with it on the matter of accountability. First, for all the interest which undoubtedly attaches to the 1964–70 period, and in particular to the IRC and the IEA, the 1972 Act remains the most recent expression of British industrial policy's most sensitive aspect. Second, it was as regards the very dimension of accountability that the Conservative Government ultimately claimed to differ from the previous Labour Administration. And third, whether or not the funds available under the Industry Act of 1972 are in fact subject to more satisfactory standards of accountability than were those earlier available under the IEA and to the IRC, it is apparent that the problem of accountability remains one of especial gravity in the field of industry and technology, no matter how governments practise intervention.

Philosophy and Objectives of Policy

Turning now to the ethos of intervention and of disengagement, it is perhaps best to let government ministers speak for themselves. Taking the Labour concept of intervention first, Mr Wedgwood Benn spoke of his Ministry, the Ministry of Technology, as 'a new kind of Government department, set up to achieve aims which had not previously been the direct objectives of official action'.[20] 'Our technological policy', he added, 'is an industrial policy', and intervention was 'not meddling, not interference, but a close, intimate, professional relationship between government and industry'. Intervention consisted, in his view, of making 'deliberate and systematic attempts to understand what industry is trying to say to us' and of 'putting yourself in a position to be of some assistance if necessary'.

In a series of speeches in the spring of 1970 the Opposition spokesman for industry and technology, Sir Keith Joseph, made it clear that a Conservative Government would wish to halt and reverse the Labour Government's policy of increasing interventionism. The same point was also firmly made in the Party's manifesto for the 1970 General Election, but what became known colloquially as the 'lame duck policy' was most unequivocally expressed by the new Conservative Minister of Technology, Mr John Davies, in his speech to the Party Conference at Blackpool in October 1970. He would not, said Mr Davies, 'bolster up or bail out companies' where he could see 'no end to the process of propping them up'.[21] He recognised that for some industries, such as aircraft production, and to a lesser extent shipbuilding, continuing government support was needed, but it was not otherwise his intention to 'throw good money after bad' by accepting an 'open-ended liability'. The actual word 'disengagement' was, strictly, the new Government's watchword with respect to the nationalised industries, but it was frequently used by commentators in 1970–71 to describe overall government policy with respect to industry. The new policy line was for a time a sharp break with the past, and it was justified ministerially by arguing that Britain's industrial weakness had in part been caused by 'some common factor' in the approach not only of the previous Labour Government, 'which showed it to a marked and exaggerated degree, but even in previous Governments of our own Party since 1945'.[22]

The compelling economic, social and political forces which eventually, and indeed quite quickly, caused the Government drastically to modify their original outlook need not be traced here. There had been many articles in the period 1966–70 which sought to discover what precisely had happened to the technological revolution promised by Labour in 1964, and it was the same now with the Conservative policy of disengagement.[23] The position eventually taken by *The Times* was that 'The Conservative attempt to create a doctrine of withdrawal from intervention in industry has been as unsuccessful as the Labour Party's attempt to create a coherent doctrine of intervention'.[24]

What are of lasting interest, since they seem certain to shape British policy towards industry and technology for many years to come, whichever Party is in power, are the reasons for the Conservative Government's change of mind. These reasons were set out by the Secretary of State for Trade and Industry in the Second Reading on the Industry Bill of 1972.[25] Having said that situations of industrial decline were 'part of the inevitable ebb and flow of a free enterprise society', in which it was 'certainly no part of Government in normal circumstances to intervene', the Minister then went on to offer a general justification of the Government's new and selective support for industry:

'The discriminatory nature of regional policy, which is its essential characteristic, can imply a positive distortion of fair competition. The alternatives are then to retire from the regional objective . . . or to provide some measure of counterpart assistance . . .

Again, there are areas of industry – particularly in the field of high technology – when the risks involved and the time taken in project development are so great as to frighten off private capital . . . There are additional considerations . . . other countries' own support of their equivalent industries . . . the fact that in many cases the industries concerned are the key to so many others . . . a need to maintain the technical and managerial competence [in a field until an international merger] can be consummated . . . inescapable contraction in an industry [where] to assent to a precipitate dissolution may occasion problems of unemployment and hardship which no Government could reasonably tolerate . . . We may also have to be ready on occasion, to provide financial assistance on a temporary basis while the situation is being fully assessed'.

In regard to his earlier views, Mr Davies remained, he said, an 'unrepenting sinner', in that he had over the years 'never failed to say that there were instances when, despite the depth of my philosophy, there were cases which defied its application'.

Political journalists were mostly agreed in their interpretation of the philosophy change contained in the 1972 Bill. Thus, David Wood referred to 'the Government's *volte-face* on industrial intervention policies', Nora Beloff to the Bill as 'the apotheosis of "consensus politics" ', and both noted Mr Davies' admission to the effect that the Government had 'bent' their own rules 'under pressure of other considerations'.[26] On the other hand, Samuel Brittan, writing from an economic viewpoint, argued that it was wrong to dwell on the Government's retreat from the principles of a market economy, because 'it was never fully wedded to them in the first place', having been from the outset 'highly selective' in applying them. He thought that the new 'Conservative-style' intervention was 'far from being the non-doctrinal common-sense that its adherents suppose', and he explained why. 'The worst fault' of the new Bill was that assistance was to be provided 'on no known principles . . . Too much discretionary power is being given to Ministers and Officials'; the regional incentives being offered were of the wrong kind; and finally, Brittan felt that the Bill provided an 'almost irresistible temptation to the Labour Party to outbid it'.[27] On Brittan's interpretation the problems of criteria and accountability had arisen yet again.

The Advanced Technology Sectors

Naturally, the interventionist policies elaborated by British Governments since 1962 have been intended to serve a number of political, economic and social ends. But what were the technological problems to which they were supposed to be addressed? There appear to have been, and to a considerable extent still appear to be, several overlapping problems, not all equally serious and some more controversial than others. Thus, a first recurring theme has been that British R & D has been too concentrated in the defence sector, and largely as a result of this, in aerospace. A second criticism, voiced for instance by Professor Blackett in 1967,[28] has been that Britain has allowed too much R & D to be undertaken in government-owned laboratories, too little in private industrial ones. A third argument holds that too much R & D in Britain, especially government-funded R & D conducted in government laboratories but not excluding other sorts, has been executed with inadequate reference to market or user considerations; the Labour Government's proposal for a British R & D Authority and the Rothschild Report on government R & D for the subsequent Conservative Government may both be seen in part as responses to this particular complaint. Fourth, it has sometimes been suggested that control as well as selection of R & D projects in Britain has been less disciplined than it might have been, even when due allowance is made for the well-understood complications of the process; the cancellations, cul de sacs and grotesque cost escalations which have occurred in some British programmes are usually cited in defence of this assertion.[29] Fifth, it is frequently said that British R & D extends over too many technological sectors, and that only a superpower can now hope to cover the whole range of possibilities. Sixth, Britain has repeatedly been blamed, both by her own nationals and by others, for being too slow to exploit her own discoveries, and too slow also to take up and apply results obtained elsewhere; this view in particular, as shown in Chapter 2, is closely related to explanations of the so-called 'technological gap'. Seventh and finally, Professor Jewkes has argued that Britain may simply have placed too much emphasis altogether on advanced technology industries.[30]

In the light of this very brief resumé of recent British technological and industrial policies and the technological problems they were in part intended to tackle, what exactly has intervention amounted to in the cases of the civil nuclear, computer and aircraft production industries?[31] In the first of these cases one might with advantage for 'intervention' read 'total involvement', because not only has there been a quasi-governmental body, the AEA, which, at least until the late sixties, carried through the great proportion of R & D and original design work on nuclear power stations, but also the country has since 1955 been wedded to successive formal 'programmes' of nuclear power plant construction, the latter constituting in effect more or less rigid commitments forced upon the customers, the Generating Boards, by the Government. The Labour Government of 1964 inherited from their Conservative predecessors problems relating both to the choice of nuclear reactor with which to continue the power programme and to the general structure of the nuclear industry; interim solutions were found in both cases but both problems were eventually bequeathed, in amended form, to the subsequent Conservative Government. Intervention in the sense of financial and other support is evidenced here by the funds made available to the AEA and mainly consumed by them, and by the maintenance of a large private industry through the commitment to a predetermined installation programme, both the AEA's budget and the size of the building programme being much larger than could have been justified by market forces at any time after the end of the fifties. Intervention in the sense of action to alter the industrial structure is evidenced by the original encouragement to industry to form omnicompetent construction consortia, and more particularly, by the later efforts to reduce their numbers, first from five to three and then, with the assistance of the IRC, to two. At the time of writing the reorganisation of these two to form a single nuclear design and construction organisation, and the suitability of the reactor selected in 1965 as compared with alternatives now available, are both continuing questions.

The two broad forms of intervention distinguished above have been particularly well illustrated in the case of the computer industry. This industry having been selected as one of the Ministry of Technology's 'bridgehead' sectors, the keynote statement on Government policy was made by the Minister on 1 March 1965.[32] There having at the start of the decade been nine British companies with computer interests, by 1967 the number was down, as a result of progressive rationalisation, to two, International Computers and Tabulators (ICT) and English Electric. The Government, determined to retain a 'substantial element of the computer manufacturing industry under British control', in 1968 helped to precipitate a merger between these two companies through the acquisition of a £3·5 millions shareholding and the promise of R & D assistance totalling £13·5 millions during the period 1968–71. In addition to thus directly facilitating the creation of the new company, International Computers Limited (ICL), the Labour Government operated a preferential purchasing policy with respect to British computers, and also mounted a series of projects and services designed to promote computer development and use in Britain. Some in fact held this Government's policies in the computer field to have been their 'most overtly successful intervention'.[33]

In the case of this industry Conservative departures from the policy laid down by the Labour administration were officially said in early 1971 to be 'comparatively minor', but there continued to be some suspicion that a 'significant if unobtrusive' change had occurred. However, in July 1972 the new Government promised further assistance of £14·2 millions to ICL, to carry the company through to September 1973, a further £3 millions in aid to the software part of the industry being announced the following month. Even so, there remained some belief that this was still only a 'holding injection of funds' while the Government worked out their long-term strategy for this industry.[34]

Again in the aircraft production industry there occurred in the 1964–70 period the twin interventionist themes of State-encouraged industrial restructuring and State-supported R & D schemes. The former was, in terms of its declared objectives, only partly successful, Rolls-Royce merging in 1967 with Bristol Siddeley on the aeroengine side, but the British Aircraft Corporation (BAC) and Hawker-Siddeley continuing their independent paths in airframe development. State financial support took the form of underwriting projects such as those for the Concorde and Jaguar aircraft, and also of providing general research assistance and assistance with the launch costs of promising new airframe and aeroengine projects, the most notorious, or perhaps in the end most famous, example of the latter by far being the financial aid and strong general support offered to Rolls-Royce in their campaign to sell the RB211 engine to Lockheed of the United States.

Conclusions

It is seen therefore that in the three 'advanced technology' industries – nuclear energy, computers and aviation – intervention had produced a certain symmetry by 1970: in the computer industry and in aeroengines there was just one British standard-bearer; in the nuclear construction industry and in airframes there were two, with a high probability that here too eventually there would be in each case only one company left. A similar concentration had also taken place in certain 'older' industries, notably of course motor vehicles. Two points seem worth noting in connection with this progressive concentration: first that the close symbiosis between government and company appears not to have been, or to be, very dependent on the actual fact of public ownership, that is, the underlying problems were not much affected by the Government's holding in ICL and in the two nuclear companies, or by the public ownership of Rolls-Royce after its 1971 nationalisation; and second, that in carrying through the successive rationalisation moves there was very little extra latitude to consider the constraints that national mergers might come to represent for the possible longer-term building of European industrial units. It is true that, for instance, in their directions to the IRC in 1968 regarding the reorganisation of the nuclear industry, the Government asked the Corporation to act 'with a special eye upon the future of the European nuclear industry',[35] but the practical effect of this injunction can at best have been marginal. So that, although this book deals with European technological collaboration, and with Britain's role in this, there must at the outset be no misunderstanding that, the dominant theme of British industrial and technological policies from 1962 to 1972 having been interventionism, the practical focus of these policies was throughout almost exclusively, and perhaps inevitably, nationalistic.

This is really a very unsurprising observation, and the fact that it could be made with similar, and sometimes greater, force in respect of all the other West European states, both puts this book in proper perspective and brings to immediate attention the core problem in collaboration. Even when the relationship between the state and industry–technology is less extensive and more circumspect than it is in Britain, as for instance in the case of West Germany, the inward-looking characteristic remains by far its most important feature. And where, as in the case of France, industrial and technological policies have been more deliberate instruments of state power than in general they have been in Britain, then their evolution – one might almost say deployment – in strict furtherance of the national interest has been still more marked. That the West

European countries have collaborated at all is therefore impressive testimony both to the imperatives of technology, in the sense of its costs, risks, complexity and inherent momentum, and to their recognition of self interest in drawing on each others' strengths. One may note rather sceptically that imperatives are not always what they seem, and that general recognition of self interest is not at all the same thing as its exact identification. And one may wonder whether Britain has not sometimes been driven too much by the imperatives, with too little reflection on the connection between general and particular self interest. This is not meant as a partisan annotation, in that the question could also be raised on the behalf of other European countries, Italy for example. One must acknowledge as well that British motives have themselves sometimes been rather mixed, and that there are certain limited grounds for expecting the motives of all the West European states to be at least a little different in the future from what they have been in the past. They will indeed have to be, or show signs of becoming, different if Europe really is to build the sort of 'complex' envisaged by the *Economist* in the extract with which this chapter began.

II   The Context of Collaboration

The 'Technology Gap'

Britain's Labour Government made the country's second formal application to join the EEC in 1967. In his Guildhall speech preceding this the Prime Minister had outlined his proposal for 'a drive to create a new technological community' in Europe, and in the one which followed he developed this idea into a seven point plan.[1] On the former occasion Mr Wilson said he could 'think of nothing that would make a greater reality of the whole European concept'. On the latter he was even more dramatic. It was to Europe's serious disadvantage that year by year the technological gap was

> ominously widening . . . there is no future for Europe, or for Britain, if we allow American business, and American industry so to dominate the strategic growth-industries . . . that they, and not we, are able to determine the pace and direction of Europe's industrial advance . . . this is the road not to partnership but to an industrial helotry, which . . . will mean a declining influence in world affairs, for all of us in Europe.

Mr Wilson made it clear that while Britain could not accept a technological community as a substitute for membership of the EEC, he felt that efforts to establish 'the essential technological component' of an enlarged Community were too urgent to be postponed until after British entry. His plan contained provisions for Anglo-European collaboration on an integrated government-industry basis in any promising technological field; for multilateral discussions between governments, paralleled by others at the CBI and TUC levels, to establish a new dynamic; and for action to bring British practice in patents, monopolies, restrictive practices and company law into line with European requirements, including the formulation of a British view on the idea of 'European' companies. There was also an intriguing commitment to help sponsor a European Institute of Technology. Mr Wilson has since written that he believes nothing did more than his original proposal to convince

Europe that Britain 'meant business', and *The Times* said after his second Guildhall address that it had 'had the warm welcome it deserves from Government and industry, both inside and outside the Common Market'.[2]

Even before this the Italian Foreign Minister, Signor Fanfani, had speculated on the desirability of a 'technological Marshall plan'; General de Gaulle had alerted his own Government to the same question and France had proposed a study by the EEC Commission of industrial and research policies in the Six. Nevertheless, in the press conference which was in effect his second veto on Britain's attempts to join the EEC, General de Gaulle argued that the problem of the gap could be overcome by the United States, if only she would end her balance of payments deficit. In spite of this second French veto, Mr Wilson and other members of the British Government returned several times during the subsequent three years to the theme of technological collaboration and already in 1967 the Foreign Secretary was stressing that only limited progress could be expected from bilateral efforts.[3]

What exactly was the gap to which Mr Wilson was referring? Or, more correctly, what beliefs did informed opinion hold about it? Because, in the not unusual absence of agreement amongst economists, politicians political commentators and political scientists frequently fall back on their own assessments, and while sometimes these assessments are sound, even when not they can be a powerful source of myth, and one is more concerned here with the political interpretation of the problem of the gap than with the true economic reality, whatever that might be. Easily the most quoted views were those of J. J. Servan-Schreiber. His book *Le Défi Américain* was published in France in 1967 and quickly became a best-seller. Translated as *The American Challenge*[4] it repeated its remarkable success in the English-speaking world in 1968, proving to be one of that small number of books which achieve a deep resonance with the mood of the moment; the mood was strengthened and the book sold. One commentator, indeed, even referred to the Prime Minister's Guildhall speech as 'La Réponse Anglaise'![5] Servan-Schreiber's assessment of Europe's situation vis-à-vis the United States was an extreme one:

We are witnessing the prelude to our own historical bankruptcy

... Fifteen years from now it is quite possible that the world's third greatest industrial power, just after the United States and Russia, will not be Europe, but *American industry in Europe* ... *the power to create wealth is the power to make decisions* ... If America is the place where decisions are made, and Europe where they are later put into application, within a single generation we will no longer belong to the same civilisation.

The language was exaggerated but others had been expressing similar sentiments, and different writers emphasised different facets of the gap. Thus for Quinn, American technological dominance, far from being directly politically stimulated, was derived essentially from two economic circumstances, the fact that the United States possessed the world's largest homogeneous market, with special governmental needs in advanced technology, and the related fact that she had so many more giant companies than Western Europe, these companies enjoying substantial advantages in terms of the integration of activities, risk-taking in R & D, investment facilities, general leverage, and so on.[6] The general economic gap was one of five sorts of gap discussed by Richardson and Park, the others being gaps in foreign investment, R & D, management, and education.[7] The foreign investment gap, and the consequent apparent ubiquity of the American commercial presence, naturally attracted a great deal of press and academic attention. Servan-Schreiber himself emphasised the astonishing growth of American investment in Europe during the 1960s, the fact that this investment, because it generally involved a real seizure of power, was qualitatively different from European investment in the United States, its strategic concentration in technologically advanced sectors of the economy, and, especially galling, the fact that on his figures nine-tenths of it was financed from European sources – '*we pay them to buy us*'.[8]

In Britain, considerable interest was aroused by Dunning's finding that, on 1968 trends, some twenty to twenty-five per cent of British manufacturing industry would be American-controlled by 1980.[9] But Dunning's figures also showed that while the average profitability of American firms in Britain was higher than that of British firms, not least because these American companies were anyway the most profitable in their home market, for various reasons this profitability gap was narrowing. Dunning judged that the overall effect of American investment, including the balance of payments aspect, had 'almost certainly been beneficial' to Britain, but he added that the country had still to come to terms with its implications for national sovereignty. On the latter point the *Economist* insisted that 'foreign capital can be kept from controlling the strategic heights of an economy without damming the flow', but it acknowledged that in the case of American investment abroad, the normal chauvinistic objection to foreign capital rapidly became one of 'positive xenophobia'.[10] The principal fear centred on the possibility of a conflict of interest between foreign firms and host government, a fear exacerbated by the option open to such firms of switching their operations between European countries. It was suggested, for instance, that not only wholly-owned subsidiaries but even firms with minority American participation were 'frequently up against stiff demands from the American partners', and that this could lead to political, economic and social disturbances, especially in crisis situations.[11]

A no less emotive issue was the suspicion that American firms would mostly choose to concentrate their research activities in the United States; only a few observers thought this unimportant.[12] Like the foreign investment gap, the R & D gap could, or so it seemed, be expressed in quantitative terms. Two much-used, and also much misused, indices were R & D expenditure as a percentage of GNP and the so-called 'technological balance of payments', the balance between sales and purchases of foreign licenses and know-how. Fuel for this fire was provided by an OECD report of 1965 which dealt with the situation as it had been in the early sixties.[13] The R & D – GNP indices were then said to have been 3·1 per cent for the United States and 1·6 for Western Europe, and the technological balance of payments to have been in the United States' favour by a factor of more than five. No one could doubt that the United States had the resources and the will to do more R & D in depth, and in more fields, than all the countries of Western Europe put together, though as Williams and others had pointed out, there was certainly no very direct relationship between the performance of R & D and economic growth.[14] McLachlan and Swann's conclusion was that leading US firms are in the strongest position to benefit considerably in a purely technological sense *over the whole range of their activities*, from actually doing a considerable amount of R & D work on behalf of government in their own organisations. The fact that relatively more of such government-sponsored R & D work is done outside the business sector in Europe cannot but attenuate the impact of science and technology upon industry there.[15]

Many, including Robert McNamara, believed that the gap was at root one of management: 'It is not so much a technological gap as it is a managerial gap . . . Modern creative management of huge, complex phenomena is impossible without both the technical equipment and the technical skill.'[16]

Diebold agreed; technology was freely available but 'You can have the most advanced technology and you can still drop the ball'. The Atlantic gap was for Diebold therefore 'not a manifestation of technological failure', in fact 'not a "technological gap" at all', but due instead to managerial disparities between the United States and Europe, and as such 'an expression of natural comparative advantage in international economic affairs'.[17] Another OECD report made the same point: 'the greatest relative advantage of US applied research as compared to that in Europe lies in the superior ability of the former to carry out concerted and sustained efforts leading from the first conception of the idea to the final development of the product.'[18]

Levitt put it even more forcibly: 'Europe's problem . . . is innovation, not creativity . . . For neither of these activities is the limited size of European markets disabling'.[19]

Technology gap, management or 'project gap', and therefore education gap, thus ran many explanations. By comparison with the American model, European educational systems were too traditional, too inflexible, incapable of fully tapping the intellectual reserves of their respective populations, and lacking in facilities. European students shunned the applied sciences, and thus the gap was 'undoubtedly related to differing value systems in Western Europe and the United States'.[20] The percentage of college enrolment overall was considerably less than half the American level, graduate and management studies were skimped, and such qualified scientists, engineers and managers as there were, were not finding their way into the key positions in the economy. It was a persuasive case, though not without its contradictions.

Whatever the precise origins of the gap, one of the most visible, and politically sensitive, manifestations of it in the mid-sixties was the phenomenon of the 'brain drain'.[21] It was easy to overlook the West's 'brain gain' at the expense of the developing world by comparison with Europe's loss to the United States. In Britain, concern mounted almost to panic. 'Britain's only burning export is that of talent,' the *Observer* lamented, not untypically. The subject had been an issue in the 1964 General Election and it continued afterwards to generate much parliamentary heat. It was analysed by academics, studied by the Royal Society, discussed by The British Association, became the subject of official and other enquiries and, in short, received constant press coverage, at least until the changes in the American immigration laws and the cuts in federal R & D budgets in the late sixties.

Whatever private satisfaction Americans may have derived from the various leads attributed to them by Europeans they were, quite understandably, anxious to play down, or where this was not possible, to rationalise, the existence of an Atlantic gap. For example, in January 1966 when Donald Hornig, Special Assistant to the President for Science and Technology, and J. Herbert Holloman, Assistant Secretary of Commerce for Science and Technology, met with European ministers responsible for these fields, the American position was essentially that there were no important inequalities in any major civil field, that the clear-cut American leads in military technology and aerospace had been established partly on Europe's behalf, and that in any case European economic growth in the post-war period had mostly been distinctly faster than that of the United States.[22] To the extent that there was an issue at all it was, according to Dr Hornig, 'almost a marketing problem'.[23] Nevertheless, President Johnson was moved in November 1966 to make a small gesture in the direction of helping Europe to bridge the controversial gap. Even if, as the *Economist* suggested, 'the only casualty so far has been national pride',[24] the Americans evidently realised the commercial and political importance to them of assuaging European fears.

The gap, whatever its causes, was seen in the last analysis as one between Europe's actual and potential performance,[25] and for this European politics were made to bear their share of the blame. The problem was neatly and amusingly summed up by Professor Casimir, Research Director of Philips. His remarks have been quoted before, but they go to the heart of the matter and will easily survive further quotation:

> Abolish the Federal Government of the US. Divide the country into its several states and make sure each has a mildly different system of taxation, a different currency, different banking and insurance laws, and different customs regulations. Regroup American minorities into as many distinct language areas as possible and in any case not less than 15, and try to make sure that whenever possible there is at least one competing minority language requiring dual language schools. Oh yes, you will need 40 or 50 distinct patent systems. Do this and the technology gap between the US and Europe will fill up rapidly.[26]

Similarly, Gilpin explained that while Britain, France and Germany could afford to worry about the gap between themselves and the United States, the remaining European countries were often as concerned with intra-European gaps, and consequently regarded cooperation as being designed as much to overcome these gaps as to bridge any intercontinental one. Gilpin was particularly severe on the Europeans. The term 'technology gap' was

> really a symbolic representation of the whole spectrum of challenges posed by a dynamic, expanding, and socially democratic society for conservative societies ruled by traditional elites wanting the power that science and technology can bring, but unwilling to pay the price of a profound social-economic transformation.[27]

The price, in Gilpin's view, involved in principle a unity of political wills, though not necessarily a supranational state, and in practice political cooperation between France and West Germany, who would then be in a position to 'impose their wills' on the lesser countries of the Six. The United States, Gilpin felt, could not be expected to do much about the problem, because the emergence of a technologically united Europe might pose a serious long-term threat to American commercial and political interests.[28] Other Americans also called for the jettisoning of outmoded pride and prejudice in Europe, Spence, for instance, arguing that the technological path of a country could only become smooth when it had come to terms with the independence and determinism of technology itself.[29]

For Britain, it was comforting to believe, as she was encouraged by her industrial and scientific writers to do, that in her application for membership of the EEC she somehow held technological aces or trumps.[30] But this conviction was by no means confined to Britain. In the words of a Council of Europe report: 'To be viable it is doubtful whether a European Technological Community could "go it alone" without the United Kingdom . . . One cannot expect the United Kingdom to agree to a European Technological Community unless it also becomes a full member of the EEC.'[31]

The point was underlined by the EEC Commission in its 1967 Opinion on British membership,[32] though one must make due allowance for the Commission's interest in having Britain a member: 'For roughly twenty years the United Kingdom has been engaged in development work of an importance such that its overall potential is today unequalled in Western Europe.'

The Commission's approval of much of this work was not without qualification, and it expected accession of the United Kingdom neither to alter the nature of the problem of getting 'agreement on objectives and a determination to develop jointly', nor probably to change 'the difficulties in the way of its solution', but it did look to British membership to 'considerably alter the Community's scope for action'. The Commission's own main proposals in this direction are outlined in chapter III, but there was during the late sixties no shortage of proposals from others also for overcoming the gap, most of them involving to a greater or lesser extent the pooling, variously defined, of European scientific and technological capabilities. And many, like the Director-General of the CBI, declared themselves in no doubt that Britain would be the greatest contributor to any such pooling.[33]

Suggestions for Bridging the Gap

The Community's scope would certainly have been enlarged by a

'European IRC', an idea strongly endorsed by the Managing Director of Britain's own Industrial Reorganisation Corporation, Charles Villiers, in a Berlin speech of September 1969.[34] Villiers disclosed that he had already had discussions with continental equivalents of the IRC, bodies which had 'experience of operating at the difficult but vital frontier where public and private sectors meet'. The discussions had centred on the 'operational principles of a new, international IRC', with a board consisting of 'successful businessmen, dedicated to the European idea', and charged to 'promote, assist and accelerate the restructuring of industry between European countries'. Villiers saw the new body as being responsible to the EEC Council or Commission, and he stressed that it would have by its style to earn the acceptance of governments, industry and the financial establishments. The idea was firmly backed by the British Prime Minister, the IRC was now able to raise money in Europe, and IRC executives were understood by early 1970 to have made some thirty European visits in part-furtherance of the basic goal.

But the IRC's own months were numbered. There was already a gulf between the words of its first report – 'there is no doubt that the IRC will increasingly have to consider supporting schemes designed to create industrial groupings on an international scale' – and the reality. The IRC's own operations had many times demonstrated both the political and social opposition to merger activity at the national level and, notably in the SKF case when this Swedish company was prevented from obtaining a dominant position in the British ball-bearing industry, the formidable problem of extending such activity to the European level. The IRC's essential philosophy with respect to the international dimension of 'high technology' industries was later summed up by one of its board members:

> on purely shortrun economic, i.e. comparative cost, considerations . . . Britain might be well advised not to be in these industries at all, or if at all, then only on a subsidiary company or subcontracting basis . . . But *if* there are to be British companies competing internationally in these industries they need to be large *and* efficient.[35]

Other proposals for bridging the gap naturally derived from the diagnosis of what it was exactly that was wrong, and they differed therefore in the same kinds of way as did the diagnoses. Easily the most persistent analyst in Britain was Christopher Layton, afterwards a member of the cabinet of M. Spinelli, EEC Commissioner for industry and technology. Layton considered government effort in advanced technology to be 'one of the largest sources of waste' in Europe, and his book, *European Advanced Technology: A Programme for Integration*,[36] published in 1969, ended with no less than fifteen policy recommendations, in his own terms an ambitious programme, and one ranging from pure science to the legal and financial support provisions for major cooperative technological and industrial policies. He continued during 1970 to list 'specific joint enterprises or policy directions in advanced technology, which would serve the twin objectives of public economy and building Europe', throughout doing his utmost to 'woo Europe' by translating her 'vague feeling' of uneasiness into detailed suggestions for political and industrial action. His stated aim was that the debate should gain momentum of its own and help gradually to give Britain 'the status of a *de facto* member of the Community'.

The ideas which Layton finally took with him to Brussels were outlined in his contribution to the later book *Europe Tomorrow*.[37] His premise remained the essential need to pool Europe's industrial and technological resources to meet the American, and soon Japanese, challenges. Europe's 'greatest weakness' was the lack of common public purchasing policies, and only clear commitments by governments could put this right, commitments supplemented by common rules or perhaps even by European executive agencies. Because in joint projects transnational companies offered 'the one means of combining efficiency with a fair cross-frontier distribution of control and effort', a merger-promoting agency was necessary in Europe, with access to adequate funds. This would enjoy 'a free hand' in less sensitive industries but require a 'specific mandate' from governments in the case of key industries. It would not, however, have powers to coerce, such as for instance Britain's IRC had possessed.[38] After common purchasing the 'second major instrument' in promoting European technology would be Community R & D contracts with industry, including the creation of a body broadly on the lines of Britain's NRDC, to oversee new technological possibilities. Other special agencies judged necessary by Layton were a European Science Foundation, 'a relatively independent executive agency, with a substantial budget', a European Advisory Council 'drawn from the best scientific and technological brains in Europe' and a Technology Assessment Centre. Finally, recognising that decision-making for science and technology can appear technocratic, and that a pooling of Europe's resources would enhance the power of the decision makers, Layton argued that 'Their choices must be conditioned, guided and controlled by democratic political discussion, backed by broad public understanding of the social choices involved,' which in turn pointed to the need for a 'powerful Science and Technology Committee of the European Parliament'.

There are, naturally, substantial parallels between Layton's ideas and those of the EEC Commission. In particular the sweeping scale of his proposals must be fully recognised, contrasting as it does with the historical fact that, in his own words, European technological cooperation has been 'the result in the main of a series of accidents, lobbies, and imperative pressures ... the uneasy result of a compromise between different national priorities arrived at individually'.

A second opinion-moulding plan was the Plowden-Winnacker scheme drawn up in 1969 for M. Jean Monnet's Action Committee for a United States of Europe, the main recommendation of which was for a new institution concerned with technological cooperation to be established in conjunction with the EEC Commission.[39] The United Kingdom Council of the European Movement was yet another group keen, especially in the person of its chairman Sir Edward Beddington-Behrens, to promote a pooling of Europe's technology.[40] One might note too Foch's essay for The Atlantic Institute, which called for a programme of cooperation in advanced technology, funds for this purpose administered by the Community itself, Britain a full Community member, and a common position vis-à-vis the United States agreed between the European countries.[41] In addition, Foch advocated a European Armaments Agency, and in his study 'European Cooperation in Defence Technology: the Political Aspect', Calmann also favoured an institution specifically concerned with this kind of technological cooperation. This institution was to encourage collaboration with the United States, including if necessary the formation of joint European-American consortia, but Calmann was anxious that it should obviate the charge that

European nations preferred to work with the Americans rather than with each other.[42]

Sir Anthony Meyer too saw a European Technological Community as 'closely inter-dependent with American technology', so that 'Britain's old bogey of a final choice between Europe or America would be conjured away'. But he also saw that it might be necessary for such a Community to 'protect its nascent technologies' by adopting in some cases appropriate 'Buy European' policies.[43] Mr Eric Moonman, though prepared to specify the initial tasks of a Technological Community, acknowledged that it could not be a case of matching American technology in all fields but of being more selective.[44] Moonman, then a Labour MP, and Meyer, a former Conservative MP, wrote a joint essay setting out what they took to be the inexorable implications of their ideas:

> a European Technological Community leads inevitably *via* a European Weapons Community to a European Defence Community (in the conventional field at least) and finally to a European Political Community . . . the logic of events takes us all very far and very fast on the way to complete political integration; much further and much faster than most people and most politicians are yet prepared to travel.[45]

Reed's analysis pointed in basically the same direction. If the ideal of a single trading community were not immediately attainable, then there might be advantage in returning to the sector approach to integration – Louis Armand's 'Federation *à la carte*' – but the real rub was that there was no single European political authority to formulate a comprehensive and consistent policy. Its creation was therefore a political imperative, for without it, the possibility of real progress was remote: 'If Europe wishes to remain a technological "third force" in the world, capable of competing against, or partnering, others on a basis of equality, some progress towards political unity is absolutely indispensable. Cooperation is not enough.'[46]

In addition to the authors mentioned here many others have also seen in the technological-gap issue a 'new reason for integration', present in muted form in some of the arguments for European unification put forward in the fifties, but only later acquiring a real driving force.[47] More recently, Basiuk has argued that unless

Western Europe manages an appropriate response to the impact of technology, then 'the region's security and its viability as a major political centre' might be 'seriously jeopardised'.[48] In his opinion the full effect of the gap is not likely to be felt until the middle or late seventies, and despite the industrial and technological complementarity of Britain, France and West Germany, the weaknesses in the existing technological superstructure of Western Europe compel him to view a continuation of technological nationalism as all too likely.

Like Basiuk, Nau has rejected any notion that the technology gap should in the seventies be regarded as a matter only of history.[49] On his interpretation, the technology-gap issue of the late sixties was preceded as a source of transatlantic dispute by the issue of nuclear weapons control in the Alliance, and has been succeeded by differing American and European views on, for instance, monetary problems and the SALT talks. All of these disputes, Nau believes, 'have common roots in a growing divergence of broader political interests between the United States and its West European allies', most West European countries having become by the mid-sixties ' "ripe" for an issue to demarcate growing political difference with the United States'. By counterattacking that the gap was one of bad European management and education the Americans were, in his judgement, seeking to defuse the quarrel because of the pressure of their other non-European preoccupations. He concludes that 'The political lesson of the technology dispute is that Europe seeks a more competitive rather than a complementary relationship'. In similar vein Schaerf had noted earlier that the technology gap was experienced by Western Europe as a power gap, and he too had thought that in raising it Western Europe had been seeking 'greater participation in a single economic system and its technology'.[50]

By 1972 the debate had certainly lost much of its earlier impetus, but it remained an issue, and it had its monuments. One such was the International Institute for the Management of Technology, formally inaugurated at Milan in October 1971. The concept of a European Institute of Technology had, both before and after Mr Wilson's reference to it in 1967, meant different things to different people, and the Milan Institute was the resultant of most of these ideas, though with the emphasis changed from 'European' to 'International' and from 'technology' to the 'management of technology'.[51] Greenberg attributes the eventual establishment of the Institute to a 'fascinating, far flung, and little-known European network', of which he has said that: 'Though political and economic union still eludes Europe, some of her leading figures in industry, government, science and education have coalesced into an informal network that has become capable of considerable influence and nimbleness in fostering multinational activity.'

The new Institute, it was planned, would offer a variety of courses in a 'thoroughly international and inter-sectoral atmosphere', the objective being 'to ensure that those who come to occupy key management positions in both industry and government during the next two decades . . . belong to the same supranational intellectual club'.[52]

By the time the Institute opened, Europe had begun to see the technology gap in a new perspective. 'Whatever happened to the technology gap?' the *Financial Times* asked, reporting a conference at The Hague; 'Technology Gap losing its sting' reported the *Guardian*, describing another held in Paris.[53] Wilshere had already concluded that 'The famous "gaps" have not been of much importance to economic growth in this generation though they exist irregularly'.[54] One reason for the change of outlook was the American defence and research cutback in the late sixties, and its lowering of American morale. There were even some Americans who were prepared now to talk of a reverse technology gap. 'Can technology eliminate US trade deficit?' wondered *Electronics International*, and *Fortune* was prepared to explain 'Why the US lags in Technology'.[55] Europe's earlier fears were also believed now to have been exaggerated,[56] and, as an example of her less defensive attitude, Nicholas Faith's book *The Infiltrators*, dealing with European investment in the United States, was welcomed by some reviewers as the sequel to *Le Défi Américain*.[57] Britain, on the other hand, was quite widely believed no longer to enjoy quite the technological advantages which had been claimed for her just five years previously.[58]

The Multinational Company[59]

Be that as it may, Europe had by this time other things to worry about, not least the new wolf, the multinational company, though for many this was simply the latest manifestation of the old American threat. This catchword concept, sometimes rendered as the 'transnational', or even simply 'international', company was invented, it seems, not so much to describe a new phenomenon but rather to symbolise a new concern, a concern evidenced by a spate of books, articles and speeches ranging from the scholarly to the intemperate. The fact that manufacturing companies with production facilities in several countries are mainly, though not entirely, American fostered the fear of the technological gap clothed in an institutional, and therefore more tangible, form. It was for instance, as Miles, writing in 1969, observed, noteworthy that European-controlled companies did not seem to evoke 'anything like the same reactions' as did American ones, at least in Europe itself.

Now, it is clear that there are economic and managerial aspects of the operations of these corporations which are of the greatest interest. And it is equally certain that their activities raise social and political questions of fundamental consequence to governments. But as regards the political matters at least, there has remained much to argue about so far as the precise effects of the 'multinationals' is concerned; and it is all too easy to exaggerate their importance. It follows that while no outline of what might be called 'gap thinking' would be complete without reference to the role of the multinationals, caution continues to be needed in appraising their political significance, if anything more especially in the case of the developed economies of Western Europe, with which this book is concerned, than in the case of developing economies.

What then are the *political* problems which multinational companies either pose now or which they might pose if the worst fears of some observers were realised? Or, more specifically, what threat might they be held to constitute which could influence European attitudes towards collaboration and cooperation?

The essence of any answer must lie in the fact that multinational companies are highly mobile international actors as purely national companies are not. It is perfectly true that national companies, especially strong ones, can sometimes, like other powerful bodies in society, offer a definite challenge to the (internal) sovereignty of governments, especially weak governments. But this is a familiar problem, well understood even by governments reluctant or unable to cope with it. But the threat in the case of multinational companies comes, to the extent that it comes at all, from outside, and the international sphere is that much more of a political jungle. What governments of countries which are host to the subsidiaries of multinational companies fear is that there may arise a clash, possibly even unintentional, between their own general objectives or specific policies and those selected by the multinational, either wholly of its own will or under the influence of the government of the country in which it has its seat, this latter, the base government, usually of course being the United States. That is, host governments face, or think that they face, 'a trade-off . . . between sovereignty and greater wealth'.

Lacking adequate and firm empirical evidence, it seems likely that clashes between the host and base governments would be politically most sensitive, that clashes arising out of direct political differences between host government and multinational company would be rare, and that clashes caused by the managerial and financial policies of multinational companies could be most common and most serious. Taking the first category of potential difficulty, as Turner says, multinationals are 'not the only instruments for applying political pressure across national boundaries', but they may well be judged to offer valuable possibilities in this direction, especially where they have been allowed to obtain a foothold in defence or other strategically significant industries. Vernon, among others, is in no doubt that 'the US Government has at times reached through the US parent to the foreign subsidiary in ways that represented a flat challenge to the policies of host governments'.[60] France and Sweden are the two European countries most frequently cited as having suffered in this way.

Of the second category of problem, while intellectual and cultural opposition to the spread of the multinationals is to be expected, and regularly occurs, the managements of the multinationals are ordinarily said to be respectful of national sensibilities, at least when the cost to them of showing such respect is marginal. Furthermore, since the multinationals are first and foremost commercial organisations, then provided markets are politically stable, one would not normally expect them to oppose the policies of governments for political reasons. In Western Europe, if not everywhere, it seems highly improbable that even the concerted efforts of several multinationals could substantially affect the fate of a government. On the other hand, it is quite possible that more American firms would have sought a base in France had it not been for the broad ideological objection shown to them by General de Gaulle, and those firms which elected to go elsewhere may perhaps be argued to have acted in a political rather than an economic manner.

The third class of difficulty caused by the multinationals contains many possibilities. Thus a multinational may be held to be responsible for capital flows damaging to the host country. Or it may attempt to evade the tax and related policies of the host government. Or its management methods may offend domestic practices. Or its international allocation of work may displease governments or unions. Or the size of its operations in a particular country may be felt to amount to an unsatisfactory and harmful distortion of that country's economy, as regards capital, manpower or specific skills. There are other possibilities still and most if not all, looked at in a different perspective, could as well be said to offer worthwhile benefits to the host. But while certain policies might enhance these benefits, governments must be expected first to safeguard themselves against dangers, and it is for this reason and, to a lesser extent, to promote the interests of their own multinationals, that European governments have been urged to make a coordinated response.

Stephenson's formulation of the pressures is a lucid one.[61] The international company is an 'intruder' in the sixteenth-century framework of nation states. Europe must manage considerably more than the 'half-hearted shuffle in the direction of internationalism' characteristic of her technological collaboration to date. Governments with advanced technology industries must 'merge their effective sovereignty, or . . . lose the capacity to support them'. They will find 'no real middle ground' between 'accepting the requirements of international industry and following the path of Castro's Cuba'. In this connection, says Stephenson, 'national independence is national impotence'.

European commentators do not agree on the need for some kind of supranational authority to provide a countervailing power to the multinationals. Alternative remedies proposed include increased industrial and economic integration, or simply better intergovernmental coordination of response to the multinationals. It would seem to be an open question as to which countries in Europe, and which industrial sectors, could hope to meet the multinational challenge by purely national rationalisation. But if continental industrial integration is advocated, then it is one of the theses of this book that, while the condition of industrial integration could in theory be envisaged as coexisting with undiminished national political independence, the process of achieving such an integration cannot. As to the more limited objective, coordination of response by European governments, it has not been shown how, in the long run, this could be to the disadvantage of any participating country, and it ought of course to be far easier to achieve than any form of true industrial integration. If it is objected that governments do not, or do not yet, see the need for such coordination, then one can only conclude that this is because the challenge of the multinationals is still judged officially to be significantly less serious than many European politicians have feared it to be. However, there appear to have been sufficient instances, both formal and informal, of competitive bidding by European governments for the favours of foreign companies, as well as certain other damaging developments, for the need already to be regarded as one which may grow, and European unions have evidently begun in principle to see things this way, as shown for instance by the formation in early 1973 of the European Trade Union Conference. The more transient problems connected with this latter development, for instance the body's relationship with third-world unions through the International Confederation of Free Trade Unions and with such trade secretariats as the International Metal Workers Federation, the question of whether or not to admit communist trade unions and the British TUC's ambiguous attitude to the EEC, all disguise, or rather postpone, the basic question of the ability of European unions ultimately to agree a common position in dealing with the multinational corporations.[62]

The multinational companies remain then, for the present, something of an enigma. But however great their promise if successfully handled, and however great their dangers if not, and whatever the myth and whatever the reality of the transatlantic technological gap, it was hardly less true in 1973 than it had been in 1967 that there existed within Europe a quite tangible and very political gap, the gap between the supranational vision and the national fact, between the aspirations of the few and the will, or lack of it, of the many, and, more specifically, between the confusion of a technological kaleidoscope and the uncertainties of some technological superplan or even superstate.

III Technological Cooperation and the European Communities

The Crisis of Euratom

Potentially the most significant formal vehicle for technological integration in Western Europe was the European Atomic Energy Community, Euratom. Euratom survives as part of the merged Communities, but it must be hoped that its experience of co-operation proves to be very atypical, because its continuing crisis of the middle and late sixties was far graver than the many serious problems which have confronted the EEC, and probably more demoralizing than the many disagreements and failures which have been registered in other European programmes in science and technology. It is strange to recall that, in the aftermath of the failure to create a European political or defence community, it was the modest sectoral integration of Euratom, rather than the ambitious general economic integration of the EEC, which was thought likely to have the better prospects. The organisation has, in recent years especially, attracted its fair share of analysis, and only the main conclusions will be repeated here; they are perhaps sufficient to indicate the sort of difficulties which can arise when objectives rise beyond collaboration to cooperation and integration.

The fundamental trouble was that Euratom, as an organisation and as a set of objectives, was the fruit of mistaken assumptions. It never escaped its 'eminently political foundations', only in appearance did it have 'all of the necessary attributes for keeping the integration momentum alive', and it was well-meaning optimism not dispassionate analysis which led to this attempt to superimpose 'a scheme for integration over the basic French interest in co-operation'.[1] Even before its birth, according to Polach, there occurred almost a 'reversal of objectives and priorities', within a year 'its significance for European integration had been seriously impaired', and he concludes that its 'modest achievements did not demand so vast an operation'.[2]

For Euratom it was unfortunate that the predicted fuel shortage in Europe never materialised. As it was, the novelty and cost of nuclear power were insufficient to prevent the growth of national programmes and the aggregation of vested interests. Another source of conflict lay in the fact that of Euratom's members, only France had a military nuclear programme, and Nieburg has also suggested that America and Britain were 'brilliantly successful' in their response to Euratom, first creating the European Nuclear Energy Agency (ENEA) as a 'counter effort to split the Continental Six and to isolate the French weapons interest', and then interpenetrating both ENEA and Euratom, helping thereby to consign both programmes 'to minor roles in subsequent intra-alliance politics'.[3] In addition, there was a French determination to deny Euratom any real integrating role, as evidenced for instance by her insistence on the replacement in 1961 of Euratom's 'too-European' President, M. Hirsch, by M. Châtenet, and this French dominance, underlined by the fact that France held the organisation's presidency throughout the decade of its independent existence, naturally produced a reaction from the other five. Another handicap was the fact that bargaining was severely restricted by its effective confinement to this one technological sector, the dynamism of which anyway exaggerated the importance of marginal advantage. The frustrations of the 'fair return' contract; too much emphasis in the assessment of contracts on specific results; too little emphasis on improved general competence; the failure to nurture the contracts of association and participation which might have given national projects a true Community element in management and finance, so that Euratom's contract activity too often amounted to a subsidy of national programmes, thereby putting at a disadvantage the countries with the weaker national programmes: these were still other factors which conspired to defeat the spirit and poison the substance of cooperation.

All these problems, and others, such as the precise rules governing the Supply Agency after 1964, whose gravity was only relatively less, together virtually crippled Euratom. Then again, quite apart from problems of cooperation, it is apparent that Euratom suffered, like the CEA in France and the AEA in Britain, from the fact that it was an institutionalised response to the need for nuclear energy development, and as such was confined to the R & D side of an effort whose centre of gravity quickly became industrial – nothing better illustrates this latter point than Euratom's infatuation with the commercially irrelevant ORGEL reactor programme.[4] The overall result was that Euratom completely failed 'to coordinate the efforts of the member countries, even less to weld them into a coherent whole'.[5] There has consequently been much duplication of reactor development within the Community, Euratom has had only a marginal involvement with the commercially important types, the organisation has not been allowed seriously to tackle the problems of the fuel cycle, in particular the provision of enrichment facilities, a true common market in nuclear technology and construction has mostly still to develop, and such transnational nuclear industrial arrangements as exist owe little to Euratom's efforts.

It has been said that 'in international organisations, difficulties – particularly budget difficulties – sometimes appear so serious because they are so public'.[6] Euratom's budget difficulties have undoubtedly been public, and there is little doubt either that they have served to express the deep-seated and almost irreconcilable differences between the member countries about the proper role of the organisation. These differences have naturally also found expression in other ways, with the results which have already been described. The differences, and the consequent budget difficulties, first surfaced in 1963, when a debate was joined on the form and scale of reductions in the second five-year research programme, reductions made necessary by the effects of inflation. Crises in international bodies can have salutary effects, but this one did not, probably because it was papered over, not solved, with the result that the organisation failed to grow in stature. The initial programmes having absorbed some $200 millions and $450 millions respectively, by the time the second programme ended in 1967 it had for some while been clear that in 1968 Euratom would have to manage with a provisional budget, and also that future programmes would have to include projects funded by only some of the participants. In October 1968 the Commission published its views on the future of Euratom, pointing out the ramifications that the Euratom crisis would have in other less developed sectors of technological cooperation. There was no reason to disguise the fact that 'the real cause of the crisis' was 'the absence of any genuine political will for joint action'.[7] For each of the years between 1968 and 1972 Euratom had to survive with one-year budgets and à la carte funding, only some of its projects being funded by all participants, so that, for example, only about half of the 1971 budget was for joint programmes.

The Commission continued to work for better things, including authority for non-nuclear research. In December 1970, following the Hague Summit, it appeared that at last a constructive step forward was possible, the Council agreeing to restructure Euratom, improve its management and increase its autonomy. But in 1971 agreement was yet again reached on only a one-year programme, the multi-year commitment wanted by the Commission being postponed until Britain became a member. Not for the first time France was the root cause of the trouble. As the only nuclear-weapon power, and a non-signatory of the Non-Proliferation Treaty, she also provided something of a stumbling block in the working out of a common position by Euratom for its negotiations with the International Atomic Energy Agency (IAEA) on the issue of inspection precipitated by the Treaty. Indeed, in view of Euratom's prolonged agony, the hardest question to answer is why it has survived at all, and why in particular France, the member most contemptuous of it, has not at some point finally destroyed it. Has it been a matter only of inertia, or have even the French suspected that in the end something worth having might spring from Euratom? The answer is probably a little of the first, less of the second, with the calculation of comparative advantage in the overall European cooperative balance supplying the best reason of all for allowing Euratom to drift, mostly irrelevantly, on.

In the light of this deep and chronic crisis, that Euratom should have achieved anything at all is remarkable, but in certain technical fields, its biology and fusion programmes for instance, it has a good deal to its credit. The low morale in recent years among Euratom's staff as their number dwindled from some 3,200 in 1967 to some 2,500 in 1972 is therefore as regrettable as it is understandable. And when the comparison is made with the position of agriculture in the Community, there is every justification for saying that 'in Europe more attention is paid to the peasants one wants to get rid of than to the technicians one needs so desperately'.[8]

The crisis and the manifest disarray in and over Euratom also made it highly unlikely that in her 1971 negotiations for entry Britain would contemplate paying any special dues, in the form of really important technical information, to join. The matter had arisen in the 1961–3 entry talks, and in its 1967 Opinion the Commission, conceding that Britain had at that time a scientific and industrial atomic potential as large as that of the rest of the Community put together, thought it 'no more than fair' that Britain should pay a special 'entrance fee' to join Euratom. But even as an arrangement to offset the adjustments Britain was seeking in other sectors, there was little case for any special entrance fee in 1967, and, Euratom having grown still weaker in the interim, no case at all for any really major transfer of information in 1971.

At the outset of her membership of Euratom Britain took, unsurprisingly, essentially the same view of the organisation as France had done for so long.[9] No other approach should logically have been expected, given that both countries have their own very large nuclear research establishments, and government research laboratories generally, and remembering also that since 1965 Britain has been trying to diversify the research work done in her own AEA laboratories so as to include a growing amount of non-nuclear research. From the British and French viewpoints, research done at the four laboratories of Euratom's joint research centre would mostly be seen as duplicating, probably with less efficiency, work done in their own national laboratories. However, despite their efforts, and those of the Netherlands, to lower still further the organisation's financial ceiling, a four-year budget of £65 millions was at last adopted for Euratom in January 1973, with all nine Community countries participating in fourteen of the seventeen projects making up the £58 millions first part of the mixed nuclear and non-nuclear package. Tight and regular reviews of Euratom's performance were part of the overall compromise reached at this time, and it is no encouragement to the morale of the organisation's personnel to suggest that, whether 1973 proves to be a true turning point in Euratom's history, or merely another temporary reprieve, will almost certainly depend much more on external political developments than it will on their own technical achievements.

Technology in General

Euratom's nuclear research apart, although the EEC, ECSC and Euratom treaties contain no formal provision for Community action in the general industrial and technological fields, the unified Commission has been increasingly concerned with this subject, the usual justification offered being along the lines that 'in all European countries the government deals actively with an industrial structure policy. This in itself is already sufficient reason for the European Commission to take coordinating action'.[10]

R & D was one of the areas of concern of the EEC's Medium-Term Economic Committee from its inception in 1964–5, and in March 1967, before their unification, the three Community Executives sent to the Council of Ministers a joint memorandum on scientific and technological progress within the Community.[11] This itemised some of the critical difficulties Europe was said to be facing, including the absence of Community company and patent laws, provision neither for tax policies to stimulate R & D nor for free capital movement, the nationalistic discrimination typically practised in the placing of contracts, and the need to coordinate national programmes so as to avoid duplication and encourage concentration. All of these issues have continued to attract criticism and exhortation from the Commission in subsequent years.

In response to this 1967 memorandum, and the work of a group attached to the Medium-Term Economic Committee, the Council of Ministers agreed in October 1967, the first such meeting of the respective Science Ministers, that the experts associated with the Medium-Term Economic Policy Committee should produce by March 1968 a report covering six broad technological sectors, transport, oceanography, metallurgy, environmental problems, meteorology and data processing – telecommunications. The West German Minister for Science was reported on this occasion as saying that there had been agreement 'not only on principles but on concrete procedural ways for achieving a coordination of policies', but others felt that since only the sixth sector, data processing, really went to the heart of the technological-gap problem,

the actual content of the resolution . . . was pretty thin gruel when compared with the enormous scale of the problem and clearly betrayed wide divergencies of opinion between the Six, not only over what should be done, how, and by whom, but also over the very nature of the Community itself.[12]

It was indeed, even at this time, necessary to take special steps to ensure the legality of Community action in this field.[13]

In the event, there was virtually no progress of any kind during

1968. Instead, the committee of experts became deadlocked after France's second veto on Britain's EEC application, and her refusal to countenance a plan to bring Britain and the other three applicants into the discussions on technological cooperation from the beginning. The Commission continued to press for action, though it did not want a separate technological community, and there were other proposals which might have broken the impasse, but it was not until December 1968 that a compromise was reached which allowed the committee to continue their work.[14] It was now provided that after the Council had reached its own conclusions on the experts' report, opinions would be sought from non-members, including non-applicants, as a preliminary to meetings of technical and financial specialists, this itself leading to a meeting, again not confined to the Six, of Ministers responsible for technology. The committee were thus able once more to take up the threads of their work, but this time under the chairmanship of Pierre Aigrain, who had in the interim succeeded André Maréchal as French Delegate-General for Scientific and Technical Research.

The committee's report, referred to as the PREST group proposals, provided for more than forty cooperative projects grouped under the headings agreed in 1967.[15] Some of the proposals involved basic research, some pointed to major industrial projects and some were schemes for further economic studies. The report was forwarded to the Council in March 1969, and in due course a formal invitation to comment was extended to Britain and the other three applicants, and to Switzerland, Sweden, Austria, Spain and Portugal. Because the proposals were eventually produced in something of a hurry, they undoubtedly comprised a 'rather uneven assortment'. The intention behind all of them, however, was to involve industry as fully as possible, to confine the projects to European-owned companies, and above all, to get something moving.[16] In the words of a committed European,

It was a brave and skilful attempt to get something – at least something – through the barriers of mutual suspicion and political ill-will which were strangling the Community . . . The only trouble was, that by avoiding strategies and principles, the Aigrain Committee necessarily and consciously avoided many of the central problems.[17]

There was initially some hope of a Ministerial Conference in 1970, but Finland, Greece, Yugoslavia and Turkey were also allowed later to join the discussions, and it was not until November 1971 that a tentative European plan, the COST group proposals, was agreed. This provided for seven projects, at a cost of some $21·5 millions, Britain joining in six and the Community as such in five, but the view that 'few of them seem likely to lead to significant industrial cooperation' was not confined to Britain, and this was therefore a very modest outcome indeed for five years' work.[18]

A further initiative by the Commission in the technological field occurred in 1970, an initiative made, as has been shown, against the background of several years of agreement in theory on the need to cooperate but failure in practice to register much real progress.[19] The Commission, persuaded by this time that the Six separately had neither the information nor the machinery to choose wisely between national, Community and international efforts in a given field, came to believe that it was desirable to separate decision-making from management and policy execution. In November 1970 it therefore proposed two new bodies, a European R & D Committee (CERD), composed of officials, academics and industrialists, and a European R & D Agency (ERDA). The first of these was to identify appropriate objectives and methods for cooperation, and the second was to be responsible for carrying out agreed projects using earmarked Community funds. These proposals had accomplished little when they were overtaken in 1971 by the negotiations on the entry of the new Community members.[20]

Industrial Policy

Technology policy overlaps with industrial policy, and in this field too the Community has found it virtually impossible to make progress. In this case, the highly successful penetration of the Community by American companies, and the contrasting inability, or unwillingness, of the majority of European companies to overcome the technical, legal, financial and social barriers to cooperation have led the Commission to emphasise the importance of cross-national mergers and the creation of a new type of company based on Community rather than on national law.[21] In the words of the Commissioner responsible: 'the Community should adopt a common industrial policy designed *inter alia* to facilitate mergers between European firms . . . Mergers are especially necessary in the sectors where technology plays a major role.'[22]

This is obviously a highly political as well as a complex legal matter, and the Commission's efforts on the legal front had been in hand for some time when, as in the technology sector, because of political disagreement, they became held up in committee. Apart from the genuine differences of view between the Six, there was again here the problem of deciding whether or not to associate the applicants with the Community's deliberations, since, like technology, industrial policy as such is not covered by the existing treaties.

In 1970 the Commission tried again, publishing both a long memorandum on industrial policy and its own draft statute for a European company.[23] The idea of a legal arrangement for a 'European' company had then been around for some eleven years, having been proposed in France in 1959, extolled in a frequently quoted address by Professor Sanders of the Law Faculty of Rotterdam University in 1960 and placed before the EEC Commission by France in 1965. It would seem that the concept of a 'European company', like that of a 'European Institute of Technology', has meant somewhat different things at different times to different people.[24] The notion of an exclusively supranational entity, while ideologically attractive as an integrative force is, it has been suggested, for instance by Mann,[25] fraught with political difficulty, that of an organisation created in only one State under a uniform European company law being equally unrealistic in his view because of the severe difficulties involved in harmonising the very different company law provisions to be found in the countries of Western Europe. The various fall-back positions have thus involved compromise, allowing for a mixture of both national and supranational law. Some, like Thompson, have regarded a suitable legal device as an 'urgent necessity'. 'It is not necessary', writes Düren, 'to spell out how the lack of Community legal regulations is impeding the process of European integration'.[26] Others have wondered what a 'European company' might be able to achieve that a national one could not, arguing that the availability of the holding-company mechanism has meant that no cross-national merger in Europe has failed for legal reasons. Often critics of the latter sort have seen tax differences as the decisive difficulty. In particular, opponents of the

Commission's 1970 proposal have felt able to condemn it on the grounds that the Community has itself neither self-sufficient law nor an adequate legal organisation to make the proposal work. For them the Commission is consequently on 'very dangerous ground in the political field'.[27]

In a no less ambitious vein, the Commission's 1970 memorandum on industrial policy, the 'Colonna plan', insisting that a common industrial development policy was indispensable to European economic unity, and to the assurance of reasonable technological independence for Western Europe, advocated action along five major lines.

First, it called for the true completion of a single market, involving in particular the final removal of frustrating technical barriers to trade, and genuinely free access to public contracts. (It actually became illegal in January 1970 for members of the Six to reserve such contracts for their own national firms, but the practice has continued because the rule is obviously extremely difficult to police, especially in respect to technologically advanced capital goods.) In conjunction with steps to achieve their first target the authors of the Colonna report wanted, second, renewed efforts to harmonise the legal, taxation and financial systems facing companies in Europe. The second of these systems was said to present the most serious difficulties in the way of multinational mergers, and the third to require the establishment of a really common capital market. As an immediate legal measure the Commission endorsed the extension throughout the Community of the French 'groupement d'intérêt économique' (GIE) concept, the main features of which are outlined in chapter V.

The Colonna plan's third proposal related to the positive promotion of multinational mergers in Europe. Figures produced for the Commission suggested that between 1961 and 1969 there had been over 1,800 mergers within member countries, but only about 250 between companies from different member countries, and that as regards more limited cooperative agreements, there had been over 4,000 of these between companies in the same country, or between a company in one of the member countries and a company from outside, but only about 1,000 involving companies drawn from two Community countries. The Colonna report reviewed the legal, psychological and political barriers to multinational mergers, and urged governments to do their best not to oppose merger activity. It even mentioned possible catalysing agents in bringing about such mergers, such as the European Investment Bank, the Commission's own credits and new Community development contracts, but the Commission, like everyone else, was privately well aware that a European body modelled on the British IRC was still too sensitive a proposition at this time for most if not all European governments.

The fourth point to which the Colonna report drew attention was the need to maximise the benefit, and minimise the harm, resulting from industrial change, by improving management, accelerating innovation and facilitating social adjustment. The report's fifth and final section concerned external economic relations, technological cooperation being instanced as one of the fields where joint action should be taken. Comparing, almost ritually now, American and European strength in such fields as aerospace, electrical engineering, electronics and data processing, the report stressed that if European efforts in these fields were not to collapse, then Europe must establish at least a threshold technical and financial capability. Existing European technological cooperation was condemned as too *ad hoc*, too little concerned with efficiency and the development of industrial strength.

It could fairly be argued that the encouragement of cross-national mergers was the major objective of both the Colonna report and of the Commission's efforts to provide for a 'European company'. The striking mergers within the Community, those between Agfa (West Germany) and Gevaert (Belgium) and between VFW (West Germany) and Fokker (Netherlands) had both enjoyed exceptionally favourable initial conditions, but, while in these cases legal, financial and political difficulties had largely been circumvented by the creation of twin organisations in the countries concerned, socio-psychological difficulties had remained. Even so, as Christopher Tugendhat observed, there were real dangers in the Commission's position: 'it elevates mergers into an object of policy . . . companies . . . should not be bullied . . . If they are persuaded to act on political rather than commercial grounds, only trouble can follow.'

From a not dissimilar outlook, Anthony Bambridge had written earlier that many Brussels officials, 'Thwarted on political unity', had 'grabbed at industrial unity as a workable first step in the right direction', so much so that they had tended, he thought, to reverse their original policy of labouring to prevent cartels. One should note in this context too the opinion of Sir Reay Geddes, chairman of Dunlop and well versed in the relevant problems as a result of that company's merger with Pirelli (Italy), that the quickest route to a transnational merger was for companies to proceed under existing law, asking for government help in overcoming particular difficulties as they arose, rather than delaying action in the hope of standard European laws.[28]

For those companies in Europe which do not see their best interests as leading to transnational collaboration, still less mergers, then action of the sort for which the Commission has pressed is perhaps not likely to be very relevant. But on the other hand, for those companies which do come to see their preferred path as lying in this direction, then, provided that their objectives do not conflict with the public interest construed now in the wider European as well as the narrower national sense, it would seem wholly desirable that these objectives should not be impeded by barriers which it is within the power of governments to remove.

In more positive defence of the Commission, there is no good reason for supposing that the merger pattern which has occurred in Europe has been the 'right' one, and the possibility of an agreement strong enough to permit the 'bullying' of companies has always been very remote. Nor is the Commission to be thought naive. It has never questioned that 'it is often not legal and fiscal barriers but practical questions of industrial compatibility and controlling power which count most'.[29] In focussing on merger policy therefore, the Commission is best seen as addressing itself to what it has taken to be a concrete aspect, and one it could consequently hope to influence, of a much larger problem with major sociological and political intangibles. In the case of the proposal for a European company especially, the Commission could hardly be blamed for trying to seize the initiative in a matter on which, unusually, it could hope for some definite French support. It has tried throughout both to take such steps as have been open to it and to call for stronger action by the Council, suggesting for example in 1971 the creation of a Committee on Industrial Policy similar to that for Medium Term Economic Policy.[30] Solid achievements, if they are to come at all, remain mostly for the future, though definite progress has now been recorded in the field of patents.[31] One cannot help reflecting that agreement might be at least a little easier to reach were there not to begin with such basic philosophical differences between the traditional industrial policies of the various European Governments.[32]

A British View

But what of Britain's attitude to a Community policy for industry and technology? There is no reason to suppose that the official British view in 1971–2 was very different from that expressed in an unofficial capacity by an assistant-secretary in the DTI at a European conference in December 1971. Mr Silver began by explaining that Britain did not regard technology policy as very meaningful in its own right, but saw it rather as an aspect of wider policies, 'above all' industrial policy. But industrial development itself was not something to be forced by Governments. The first priority was simply to get the climate right, and Community development contracts, for instance, came lower down the list of priorities. In spite of their excellent achievements Britain had become 'somewhat disenchanted' with her advanced technology industries, in particular because they had had to compete in markets which were too small, and because they faced heavily subsidised American and Japanese opposite numbers. An appropriate Community public procurement policy might help in the first respect, but undertaking a permanent subsidy was only sensible if an industry's products were essential to Europe's economy or defence, and if there were a risk of being held to ransom. On this account Britain was 'somewhat dismayed' at some Community thinking; Europe's way forward must surely be specialisation country by country, and the avoidance of prestige projects.[33]

With respect to Community machinery, Mr Silver saw no need for special legal and institutional arrangements for technology. Britain regarded, 'with some detached amusement', the Community's difficulties in giving effect to its decisions, but the idea of a central authority deciding upon the geographical distribution of research or the industrial division of development was 'simply not acceptable'. On the contrary, Britain believed in an *ad hoc, à la carte*, approach to technological cooperation. And, given the political realities, an extension of the Community's successful contracts of association and a more piecemeal approach might be the most appropriate method for the Commission to follow in the industrial field, a field in which Britain looked forward to a substantial net income to counterbalance the outflow of funds which the Community's existing policies entailed for her. There was no reason, Mr Silver indicated, to suppose that Britain would be less nationalistic than the existing members of the Community had shown themselves to be, and he cited three contemporary European technical projects to underline his point. Britain, he thought, had not regretted the collapse of the giant computer scheme put forward in the Aigrain plan, she had warned the Community that unless the proposed European weather centre were established at Bracknell, then she might not feel able to contribute financially to the same extent, and British recognition of the need to create a software information centre at Euratom's Ispra centre was conditional on a major Community contract going to her own national computing centre at Manchester. Mr Silver was in fact especially severe on Ispra. Why, he wondered, had no cost benefit analysis of it been done; the ways of the Community in this case had for Britain a 'certain frightening quality'. Not that Britain wanted to be thought negative in her attitude to technology. It was simply that many in Britain felt that the Community spent too much of its time 'discussing policy without regard to political reality', and Mr Silver hoped that in this area the Community might 'perhaps adapt a little to us rather than we adapt to the Community'.

Whether or not Britain's method of dealing with technological questions could, as Mr Silver hoped, be regarded as a commonsense one, it is abundantly clear that his sort of hard realism could not be very welcome in Commission circles. The possibility of synthesising a dynamic accommodation between the two positions is examined later. Here it is sufficient to note the cause of the clash; the fact, first, that the views of national officials are based, and must be based, on an orthodox reading of the national interest, their approach being buttressed by the knowledge that the national officials of the other European countries are acting in a precisely similar way; and second, that the Commission is proceeding on its own assessment of what might constitute the European ideal. It should also be recognised, for instance in considering Britain's attitude at the Paris Summit of 1972, that views of the general sort expressed by Mr Silver probably run too deep and are held too widely in Britain for any sudden change to be likely.

1972: the Commission's View and the Paris Summit

At the beginning of 1972 then, a scientific, technological or industrial policy for the Community was 'still only a hope'.[34] Euratom's difficulties and the very limited results of the work done by the PREST and COST groups were separately and together bound to provoke a certain scepticism, if not outright cynicism, and even by the end of the year the PREST group were forced to describe the fruits of their own work as a meagre return on the 12,500 man days and $2 millions invested.[35] In the course of 1972, the negotiations on entry of the new members having been concluded, new proposals on industrial and technological policy began again to emerge from the Commission, the new keynote document being submitted to the Council in June. Whatever the results which ultimately flow from this further initiative, it well deserves a brief interpretive summary here, as representing the distillation now of some seven years of growing effort on the part of the Commission.

The Commission's fundamental objective is seen as the making of Europe into 'a technological force in the world', the European nations acquiring 'more power and negotiating capacity', and thus playing a significant international role, through the coordination of their joint potential.[36] Once more in 1972 the Commission insisted that the joint action which had become so characteristic of Europe required to be improved upon, in that the previous fifteen years had been 'an experimental period, rather than a period of achievement'. The Community could not hope, the Commission admitted, to 'do or centralise everything'. Indeed, the need for a policy flexible enough to permit all types of cooperation was clear, and the creation of a scientific and technological community could at best be gradual. Nevertheless, the Community had to be given new powers, and it deserved them, possessing already the basic infrastructure for action, and offering 'the most coherent framework' for coping with discrepancies between national inputs and outputs to European-level projects. The Commission thought it 'reasonable, if not essential', it said, that Community activities in future not be concentrated in the agricultural sector, and it redefined the instruments it held to be necessary for its purposes.

The need was restated for a European committee of scientific advisers (CERD), headed by a chief scientific adviser and supported by a small 'think-tank'. The Commission's role, it was explained, would involve in particular bringing together senior national officials in a periodic 'Committee for Consultation and Coordination', while decisions would be taken by the Council of Ministers, acting as a 'Council on R & D'. On the policy execution side a European Science Foundation was again called for in the area of fundamental research, but the Commission now modified its 1970 proposal for a European Research and Development Agency (ERDA), conceding that this should perhaps best be regarded as a 'medium-term solution', and that 'partial and provisional solutions' were possibly preferable in the immediate future. The Commission also now sought some £8 millions for the establishment in 1973 of Community innovation and development contracts, indicated that it planned to work out, with the European Investment Bank, specific proposals regarding the provision of venture capital by the Community and said that it intended to make more specific proposals in due course with respect to the aviation, data processing and communications industries. A proposal for a 'marriage bureau' for medium and small firms was also known to be immediately in hand.

Quite clearly, despite the modification of the ERDA concept, and given also the absence of concrete proposals in the advanced technology sectors, the Commission was in 1972 seeking major new responsibilities. Had it demonstrated the need for such powers? In the logical sense quite possibly yes, but then the need for common action had long been, very largely, common ground. But in the political sense, the only sense which in practice matters, even more certainly no. In no document, including this one of 1972, had the Commission explained in detail how, in carrying out a common R & D programme, it would meet the inevitable national objections. The Community's machinery is not a uniquely suitable framework because the Commission says that it is.[37] Unless or until national governments are prepared to see the Community in this way, Europe's network of agreements, however incoherent, and the scars which mark the failures to agree, alone constitute the living reality of European collaboration. By this token it may be right to criticise them, but they should probably not be condemned until their replacement is imminent. But, of course, one must recall yet again that the Commission has no alternative, having defined for itself the nature of the European ideal, than to devote itself to the realisation of this.

In the light of all that has been said so far, and the reservations of British civil servants notwithstanding, it is easy enough to understand why those who had come to despair of the Six's rate of progress in industrial and technological matters, should also have come, if sometimes as a last hope, to look to Britain to furnish a new momentum.[38] This in fact Britain appeared ready to do following the position taken by her Prime Minister at the Paris Summit of 1972. The Conservative Government had repeatedly stressed the significance of the European dimension of their industrial policy, and in the words of the Minister for Industrial Development: 'As we move into Europe there is no doubt that the role of Government will be less that of holding the ring. It will more often have to be in the ring as a partner of industry.'[39]

The Prime Minister Mr Heath had himself previously said that the enlarged Community 'must' provide for the emergence of vigorous 'European' firms, and that it 'must' encourage the combination of national capabilities. In his address to the Paris Conference he went on to stress that,

> an effective regional policy is an integral part of the Community's work ... We need an industrial policy ... a deliberate plan and a prescribed timetable. I hope this conference will enter into clear commitments on both these points ... only thus will we be able to see the European economy integrated.[40]

The communiqué issued after this Conference gave some evidence that Mr Heath's efforts had been rewarded. A 'high priority' was to be given to correcting the Community's 'structural and regional imbalances', and a Regional Development Fund was to be established before the end of 1973. With respect to industrial policy proper, the essential objectives of the Colonna plan were endorsed, together with a proposal to develop common science and technology policies, and it was firmly stated that the Community's institutions were to work out a programme of action and a precise timetable before 1 January 1974.

Britain as a member of the EEC will undoubtedly continue to have some special interest in persuading the Community to give a higher priority to industrial, technological and associated regional policies.[41] Two reasons above all supply this interest. First, Britain has serious existing and incipient regional industrial imbalances. Second, her industrial and technological competence is nevertheless both deep and extensive, and she can reasonably expect her private and even her public industry to play a major role in Europe if not too many political and commercial obstructions are placed in the way. She has a very sound logical case going for her. If Europe wishes to continue to grow rich, then it is the performance of European industry which alone can make this possible. And even if the growth is to be tempered with an evolving concern for the environment, for resource management, and for the quality of life generally, then it is a new European dimension to national and industrial policies which may best facilitate this. But there is plenty of room for slips between the cup of logic and the lip of action, and some at least of the lessons are already there for those who chose to study them in the past record of the EEC.

It remains to be seen then whether in this sector the Paris Summit of 1972 really did represent a new departure.[42] It was, one remembers, Chesterton who described optimism as the noble temptation to see too much in everything, and Bradley who said of pessimism that where everything is bad, it must be good to know the worst.

IV   The Commitment to Collaborate

The Focus on Advanced Technology

The technological fields which, because of the costs and risks attached to them have so far seemed most suitable for European collaboration are aviation, space, nuclear energy and computers, and in the first three of these at least European Governments have made some important commitments. In addition, there are or have been collaborative defence projects outside the aviation sector, mostly at the intergovernmental level, and collaborative arrangements have also been made, or possibilities explored, in 'older' technological sectors, with varying degrees of public and private involvement, for example the Fiat-Citroen and Volvo-Daf links in motor vehicles, that between SAVIEM and MAN in trucks and the proposed Channel Tunnel. And as is well known, important collaborative steps have also been taken in the scientific field, notably in the domain of high energy physics. On the other side of the balance, one ought not to forget the number of ideas, especially in the defence field, which have perished stillborn.

Within the four so-called 'advanced' technology sectors, Britain's commitment in practice to European collaboration has, broadly, followed the order given above, having been greatest in aerospace, where government expenditure alone averaged over £50 millions per annum during the sixties,[1] and least in computers. This is therefore a reasonable order to follow in discussing 'commitment', though throughout examples are drawn from all four fields, and from others, where it seems that there is a useful point to be made.

But since this order is one of convenience rather than of logic, one should properly make at least two qualifications at the outset. First, concentration here on the four 'advanced technology' sectors is certainly not intended to imply that the author subscribes to the view expressed in 1966, by the then French Science Minister, to the effect that 'Europe will be made by the atom, space, aeronautical construction and computers, or it will not be made'.[2] On the contrary, there are times when, on reflecting on what has so far been accomplished in these fields, one is almost inclined to say that, if it is through collaboration in these sectors that Europe must be 'made', then it will not be made at all. The second qualification concerns the need to distinguish between collaboration in science and in technology, and between collaboration in defence technology and in non-defence technology. On the evidence, the former distinction would seem to be rather more clear cut than the latter, but in both cases the differences appear to be matters of degree, that is, of how much political sensitivity, rather than of kind, in that there is always some political element involved.

One can usefully defend this second assertion by considering a recent study of West European collaboration in weapons procurement. The authors of this study, Simpson and Gregory, naturally find the main original impetus for defence collaboration in economic logic and limited defence budgets – the need to spread R & D and production costs while keeping total annual expenditures within politically acceptable limits. They also adduce other reasons for the practice, including the advantage of standardisation, the enhancement of national capability in specific technical sectors, support of existing workforces and utilisation of existing expertise, and saving on foreign exchange costs. But they say as well that collaboration 'can be seen as a means of increasing or retaining political influence, cementing amicable relationships, and underlining in a visible manner new departures in foreign policy'. And they submit that in Europe the process of collaboration has been 'transformed' by its 'politicisation' and by 'its possible identification with a nascent European nationalism', while for Britain they see it as having had an especially symbolic connotation. Their overall conclusion is then that: 'The area of cooperation impinges on values that have traditionally been of supreme importance to the nation state. The result has been a process with broadly based, if diffuse, political support, rather than merely a narrow economic or military rationale.'[3]

It is true that questions of defence traditionally touch national sovereignty more closely than do questions of commerce, but this difference is partially redressed by the political importance which has come to be attached to comparative industrial strength in Europe during the post-war period, a period, what is more, during which European defence has at times seemed to possess a slightly unreal quality because of the nuclear and superpower realities. If only the spirit of this switch of emphasis is acknowledged, then what Simpson and Gregory say of West European collaboration in weapons procurement would seem to apply with little change to civil technological collaboration as well. Consequently, it has not seemed necessary in the analysis which follows to draw a sharp line between defence technology and everything else.

The Aircraft Industry

As regards European collaboration in aircraft development, one need perhaps say least about the Concorde agreement.[4] There appeared from the first in this case to be a sound enough technical basis for collaboration and, with Britain at the time making her first application to join the EEC, the project was evidently thought a very opportune one politically. It is a matter of history, and in Britain a long-standing grievance, that this Anglo-French commitment was quickly followed by the first French veto of Britain's EEC application. The attempt by the Labour Government in 1964 to have the programme re-examined, and no doubt cancelled, is detailed below. Thereafter the aircraft became something of a political albatross. The rueful admission in May 1971 by Mr John Davies, as Secretary of State for Trade and Industry, that 'the truth is that at this stage it would indeed be very unwise to do other than proceed', could have been made at any time after the 1964 attempt at nullification had failed. Mr Wedgwood Benn's position had been that Concorde would decide its own future, and his immediate Conservative successor as Minister of Technology, Mr Geoffrey Rippon, said virtually the same thing.[5]

Concorde has understandably received most of the public attention, but there is also much of interest in the five continuing Anglo-French military projects, the Jaguar fighter, Martel missile and Lynx, Puma and Gazelle helicopters, and in the Anglo-French variable geometry aircraft (AFVG) and Airborne early warning aircraft (AEW), with both of which the two countries failed to continue. To begin with, the Martel example shows above all how good mutual confidence between the two companies concerned can greatly smooth the paths of the respective governments, the AFVG by contrast how the highly independent efforts of a private firm, the

French Dassault company in this case, can help to destroy a seemingly attractive collaborative project.[6]

The AFVG case is an especially important example in the context of commitment, in that the two governments were at no stage involved to the same extent. The aircraft was seen by British Ministers as operationally and industrially the core of the country's long term aircraft programme, and as part of an answer to the American technological challenge.[7] Dassault however, unhappy with British design leadership on the AFVG, and with the administrative complexities of an intergovernmental programme, managed to fly their Mirage G, an aircraft similar to, but not identical with, the AFVG, before the provisional Anglo-French understanding was due to become a firm commitment. As a result, few in Britain believed that the subsequent French withdrawal had been, as France insisted, occasioned entirely by budgetary factors, and in due course the single-engined Mirage G, having proved the variable geometry principle, evolved into the twin-engined G8, like the AFVG would have been, a multi-purpose aircraft. Although the joint feasibility study for the AFVG went into more technical detail than would have sufficed for a purely British aircraft, it has been widely believed that for France, the AFVG was never really more than 'just politics', tentatively entered into to make French design leadership on Jaguar more palatable to Britain. The French Government had after all awarded Dassault a contract for the Mirage G at much the same time as they became caught up in the AFVG project, they were all too clearly wavering more than six months before they finally pulled out of the latter, and they afterwards ordered from Dassault two prototype G8s.[8] In this connection too, it has frequently been alleged by some British observers that France has nursed a grudge against the United Kingdom in aerospace for not buying the Atlantique, Transall, Caravelle or Spey-Mirage aircraft, in spite of substantial French purchases of British aircraft and engines.[9]

However, if the short-term outcome of the AFVG case was damaging to Britain, the medium-term outcome seems not to have been very favourable either for France or for Dassault, in that the UK later went on to reach agreement with Italy and West Germany on the multi-role combat aircraft (MRCA). Dassault's claim that the latter will be several times more expensive than a Dassault variable geometry equivalent need be has remained disturbing. But if, as appears to have happened, Dassault have 'ended up with an excellent prototype without a market' then they surely have 'won on technology but lost on politics',[10] assuming that is, that if the Dassault VG and the MRCA both go into production, the Dassault VG fails to establish an advantage in sales to third parties, not an entirely comfortable assumption remembering foreign sales of the Mirage III and V. In any case, Europe as a whole, it is apparent, reaps no advantage at all from this duplication.

The Atlantique, and also the Fiat G91, both NATO inspired aircraft, illustrate what can happen when a project is settled on the basis of a design competition between firms from several countries without any pre-arranged government commitment. The choice having fallen on an Italian company in the latter case, the French, though not without some justification, refused to take the aircraft. And when the French Breguet company received management responsibility for the Atlantique, Britain, the United States and Canada declined to buy it, though the United States made a financial contribution and remained on the steering committee, later managing, under the unanimity rule adopted, to prevent a major export sale of the aircraft to South Africa. The 'outstanding lesson' to be drawn from the Atlantique example in particular, it has been said, is that 'industrial participation in the production of a project of this kind must carry with it a positive commitment to purchase the equipment or to pay a substantial penalty'.[11]

But the depth of a collaborative commitment may well, even at the outset, need to be more fundamental than this. Thus, one weapons procurement expert argues that 'for it to be effective, collaboration must take place at all levels . . . [including] the levels at which decisions are made on defence policies'.[12]

Rather less ambitiously, Britain's Defence Secretary said in 1967 that it was his impression that when there was a 'clear common interest to be achieved which is accepted in principle in advance', then it was possible 'to work out agreements in detail and stick to them'.[13] Or, as the Plowden Report on the British aircraft industry put it, 'Harmonising requirements is the key to the problem'.[14] The most recent example of this in Europe has occurred with the Alpha Jet, where it proved possible to reconcile the originally quite different requirements of the French and German airforces by a programme review at an early stage.

As explained above, Britain's ideas for a variable geometry aircraft, kept alive by a very sympathetic Ministry of Technology, eventually took concrete shape as the MRCA.[15] Sufficient harmonisation to allow collaboration on this aircraft was possible for Britain, West Germany and Italy, but in the process Belgium, Canada and the Netherlands dropped out, either because the planned aircraft did not meet their needs, or because it was likely to be too expensive, or because its time scale was wrong, the three criteria which the House of Commons' Expenditure Committee have described as 'the most common obstacles to any collaborative project'.[16] Strong views have sometimes been expressed that for best results there should be no more than two participating countries in this sort of project. Mr Healey, for instance, when Defence Secretary had this preference, on the grounds that with more than two it became very difficult to agree on specifications.[17] The 1966 Statement on the Defence Estimates echoed this: 'progress in multinational development has so far been disappointing. We have had better success with bilateral arrangements'.[18]

If agreement to collaborate on an aircraft is eventually reached, then the very fact that so many problems have had to be overcome to bring it about can make the commitment thereafter an unusually binding one. This has been demonstrated for example by the Jaguar programme. Had this been a purely national venture, then 'a publicly declared intention to buy 200 aeroplanes right at the outset . . . would have been inconceivable'.[19] Other interesting consequences followed.[20] When the project was initially undertaken the proposed aircraft was viewed by Britain as a supersonic trainer for service about 1970. British officials thought later that the French had made a 'really substantial compromise' in agreeing to develop a super- instead of a subsonic aircraft. Their own compromise, in settling for a fixed wing instead of a variable geometry configuration, they ranked as 'virtually a non-existent' one, because variable geometry had at the time been more a philosophy than anything more concrete. Britain having entered into the commitment, two major developments then radically altered her plans for Jaguar. First, the P1154 programme was cancelled and the RAF therefore came to feel that they would need some other new aircraft for close support work; and second, it was found that as a trainer Jaguar would be too expensive, and was anyway more advanced than it needed to be. The main projected role for the aircraft was as a result switched from training to operational close support. The question which later occurred to the Public Accounts Committee was naturally, had Britain in this instance engaged in collaboration prematurely? The Ministry very firmly repudiated any suggestion of this, but in rather grudgingly accepting their answer the Committee remarked severely that 'but for fortuitous circumstances the Ministry would have found themselves with an unnecessary, over-sophisticated and expensive supersonic trainer'. They trusted, they said, that the Ministry would in future 'be able to obtain cost-effective aircraft from good planning rather than good fortune'.

To begin development of a collaborative military aircraft project full government backing is undoubtedly necessary, but in the civil sector governments are reluctant to direct airlines, and harmonisation is correspondingly held to be more difficult to achieve. The European airbus project provides the natural example of this. This project is also of interest as an instance of a British loss of commitment, and because of an awkward question of government propriety which it raised in Britain.[21] The airbus project had travelled a somewhat tortuous path both technically and politically for more than five years when the Labour Government announced their effective withdrawal in the spring of 1969. There were at that time fears that British engines would not be first choice, worries about rising costs, uncertainties about orders, and a reluctance to accept yet again French design leadership. In December 1970, having been invited to rejoin, the Conservative Government declined on what were stated to be economic grounds, but this second decision had to be reached in a situation made extremely difficult on three counts. First, the Government were already supporting two highly expensive civil aircraft projects, Concorde and the RB211 engine for the Lockheed Tristar; second, the European airbus was by this time firmly scheduled to have American General Electric engines; and third, it appeared commercially unwise to reject the request by the British Aircraft Corporation (BAC) for support for their BAC311 in favour of the hybrid European project.

This third complication demonstrates the domestic commercial embarrassment goverment can expose itself to by its choice of agent in collaborative projects. BAC had matched the early European airbus proposals with their 211 scheme, and the A300B, as the airbus became after 1968, with the 311. In their announcement the Conservative Government declined to support both the A300B and the BAC311, because, they said, of the size of public investment involved. As they acknowledged, one of the dilemmas with which they, and no doubt the previous Labour Government too, had been faced, was that aiding BAC would have involved them in supporting a project in direct competition with the airbus, in which another British company, Hawker-Siddeley, were engaged without assistance from public funds. The question of Hawker-Siddeley's right to equal treatment had already arisen earlier when it emerged that BAC, the Government's agent for Concorde and Jaguar, would again in the AFVG scheme be the British participant. The Labour Government's defence on that occasion had been that the situation was one dictated by considerations of work load and expertise,[22] but since then the MRCA also had begun with BAC as the British element. The case well illustrates therefore how the balance of advantage in design leadership can be a national commercial, as well as an international political, problem. At least by contributing neither to the BAC311 nor to the A300B the British Government avoided the charge of being lukewarm Europeans. To the extent that British European Airways (BEA) had a free choice, the Government were passing to them the invidious task of deciding for their needs between the Lockheed Tristar, with Rolls-Royce engines, and the A300B, with Hawker-Siddeley wings, and in 1972 BEA chose the former.[23]

A slightly whimsical comparison suggests itself between the A300B-BAC311 case and Britain's hesitation, at about the same time, as to whether or not she would contribute towards the new particle accelerator planned for CERN.[24] The Labour Government, in concluding that the expenditure on the latter was not justified, were 'particularly concerned at the effect which participation might have . . . on the balance of resources in Britain between high energy physics and other scientific activities'. The Conservative Government, reversing this decision, with respect it is true to a considerably modified programme, announced that 'A complete appraisal of priorities within the civil science budget has made it possible for the cost to be found without additional public expenditure'. One is tempted to conclude that in the A300B-

BAC311 case the lobbies cancelled each other out, but that in that of CERN, eventually, they did not.

The official British attitude towards collaboration with Europe on aircraft development cooled somewhat in the late sixties, and new joint projects were noticeably absent, though at the private level BAC, MBB (West Germany) and Saab-Scania (Sweden) announced in 1972 the formation of Europlane, through which they planned to collaborate on a quiet short take-off and landing civil aircraft (Qstol) and Hawker-Siddeley became engaged with VFW-Fokker (Netherlands-West Germany) and Dornier (West Germany) on a similar project. These were private ventures, but it was accepted that government financial assistance would in due course be necessary for both. The general evolution between the middle and late sixties of prevailing British views on aviation collaboration is well illustrated by comparing the Plowden and Elstub Reports. For the Plowden Committee,

> most future development projects must be cooperative ventures . . . a weakness of past policies has been that Britain has tended to associate at random with all comers on the merits of individual projects . . . the policy of collaboration . . . should be given a clearer sense of direction . . . [and] a far more powerful momentum.[25]

But for the Elstub Committee:

> The attractions of collaboration . . . have tended to obscure its disadvantages. These stem mainly from the length of time taken to reach decisions at Government level, and from the fact that considerations of national interest and balancing financial contributions do not necessarily result in the most efficient division of the work. It may be that collaboration can only be really effectively achieved if the initiative in seeking opportunities and negotiating partnerships is taken by industry.[26]

This Committee went on to hope that government would then support these initiatives, recognising that in the case of military projects it was probably inevitable that governments should continue to lead. They realised, they said, that in all cases where it was investing money a government had a complex equation to solve involving suitability of the product, share of the work and effect on domestic industry, but they also had in mind that collaborators could later turn out to be, once more, competitors.

After 1967, the British Government in fact came under strong pressure from the aviation lobby to abandon an exclusive commitment to European projects, on the grounds that it 'hopelessly compromised' the British hand in negotiations. 'To negotiate satisfactory terms', the Air League asserted, 'it is essential to have credible options, including, in the final analysis, the possibility of going it alone'.[27] In mid-1969 the possibility of purely British projects was reopened by the Minister of Technology, and a junior minister now explained that 'where possible we want to collaborate . . . But the first consideration is the prospect of a profit'.[28] The political milestone of a new independent British project was eventually reached in 1971, with the announcement of an award to Hawker-Siddeley of a contract for the HS1182, broadly a rival of the Franco-West German Alpha Jet. This was a contract which also helped to restore the balance of public support as between BAC and Hawker-Siddeley.[29] At the time of writing the British Government had not decided whether they would also offer Hawker launching aid for their HS146 project. Apart from the political disadvantage that it was scheduled to have American engines, this aircraft project was opposed in Europe as being in competition both with the VFW-Fokker 614, an aircraft being built collaboratively by West German, Dutch and Belgian firms, with Rolls-Royce-Snecma engines, and also with the Fokker 28 Fellowship, another collaborative development, this time involving directly the British firm Short Brothers and Harland, as well as again having Rolls-Royce engines. Given their highly successful commercial performance, that Hawker-Siddeley were in general deserving of support could hardly be questioned; that the HS146 proposal was not an easy one for the British Government to approve was no less apparent.[30]

The selection of the Rolls-Royce – Turboméca Adour engine for the HS1182 allowed some slight flavour of collaboration to persist, but this contract was none the less a milestone. Concorde's function as confirmation of Britain's commitment to Europe has been mentioned above, the parallel case of the European Launcher Development Organisation (ELDO) is dealt with below, and the Anglo-

French military aircraft projects followed these leads. Even in the case of the DRAGON reactor project it was later said that, despite Britain's involvement in CERN, 'We still felt that the setting up of an international project of a technological character would be taken as an acid test by our European partners of the feasibility of co-operation with us'.[31]

But by 1971 the Government were prepared to insist that Concorde was 'certainly not part of the bargaining with regard to the Common Market', and that there was 'absolutely no question' in any sense of its being played off against the RB211.[32] These replies and the HS1182 could together be seen as symbols of a new independence. By contrast, formal European collaboration on aeroengines seemed at the same time to be gathering a certain new strength, though again there were serious complications.

There had naturally already been a substantial amount of collaboration on engines as part of the various government-inspired aircraft-production programmes. Thus, Rolls-Royce had linked in 1960 with MTU (West Germany) on the RB193 for the West German VAK 191B STOL fighter, with KHD (West Germany) on the T112, an auxiliary unit for this same aircraft, with Snecma (France) in 1962 on the Olympus for Concorde and in 1965 on the M45 engine series, with Turboméca (France) in 1966 on the Adour for Jaguar and the Anglo-French helicopter engines, with Fiat (Italy) and MTU in 1969 for the MRCA's RB199, and on more conventional lines had licence agreements with still other European companies, such as Volvo Flygmotor of Sweden. Rolls' experience of big advanced engines, for which development costs can now reach £200 millions, had gradually led them to favour the notion of a European aeroengine combine, and even as he refused to rejoin the European airbus project Mr Corfield, as Aerospace Minister, approved Rolls' idea, later speaking of 'some sort of merger' between the company and Snecma.[33] In the spring of 1972 meetings began between several of the above-mentioned companies, with the aim of gradually rationalising the European aeroengine situation, perhaps allowing the separate companies to keep their identities while providing for the consortium as a whole, or such members of it as wished to, to tackle new projects in concert.

There followed an excellent example of the role of commercial manoeuvring in the formation of international commitment, because Snecma, a nationalised company, backed by the French Government through their five-year plan, now reached an agreement for the development of a 'ten tonne' engine, 'Despite, or perhaps because of, French government awareness of supposed American dominance in technological industry',[34] with the American General Electric Company, Snecma to have design leadership. This was evidence to much of British opinion that France was determined not to recognise politically any technical lead held by Rolls-Royce. Not until later in 1972, after the American Government had decided to frustrate the Snecma-General Electric link, did a real possibility arise of involving Snecma fully in the embryonic European aeroengine consortium.[35]

Apart from the projects already referred to, there have been a few more general signs of a European-level approach to aviation. Two one might mention are the efforts of the Association Internationale des Constructeurs de Matériel Aérospatial (AICMA), which through working parties and otherwise has helped significantly to lay the foundations for common action between eleven European countries, and the European Organisation for Civil Aviation Electronics (EUROCAE), which brings together electronics companies and governments for the purpose of translating International Civil Aviation Organisation (ICAO) recommendations into technical standards, which can then form common mandatory requirements for the member countries. And, since the difficulties of harmonising civil aircraft requirements have been stressed, note should also be taken of the airline groupings, the KSSU and Atlas organisations, bringing together KLM, Scandinavian, Swissair and UTA, and Air France, Alitalia, Lufthansa, Iberia and Sabena respectively. The links in these cases range from aircraft specification and appraisals to common training and maintenance, and it has been suggested that although the implicit power of these organisations was already evident in KSSU's selection of the McDonnell Douglas DC10 in preference to the Lockheed Tristar, their significance is still waxin.[36]

It will also be realised that the specific collaborative aircraft projects which have been mentioned here were themselves preceded by many intra-European licence agreements as regards both airframes, engines and complete aircraft. Other developments too have encouraged collaboration. There was, for instance, the 1959 agreement which allowed West Germany, Belgium, Italy and the Netherlands to build the American F104 fighter aircraft under licence, and which helped facilitate a decade later the Fokker-VFW link; there was the progressive arrangement worked out between Fokker, Breguet and Sud (France), which later led to collaboration on the European airbus, and there was the Dassault-Fokker link, which followed Belgium's purchase of the Mirage V and Dassault's investment in the Belgian firm SABCA, largely owned by Fokker. Altogether, it is hardly surprising that calls for rationalisation in the European aircraft industry have been so numerous in recent years.[37] These calls have come both from within the industry and from political sources. In Britain, members of the Conservative Government have spoken of the need to go 'a long way further' than *ad hoc* collaboration 'to some more permanent form of industrial association', a development which one of them suggested might receive a 'political and psychological boost' on Britain's entry into the EEC.[38] A good deal more controversially, Layton has written of the need to 'consider how the restructuring of the airframe industry in Britain can best serve [the] common aim' of European airframe and aeroengine companies, meeting with the response that 'The practical steps to build Europe are vitally important. Anyone who advocates one-sided concessions does an ill-service to that end'.[39] It is in this context that a merger between Britain's main surviving aircraft firms, BAC and Hawker-Siddeley, has for several years remained a subject of discussion. This will have been one of the matters covered by the (unpublished) Marshall Report on the British aircraft industry, completed for the Secretary of State for Trade and Industry in 1972.[40]

The institutional mechanism through which a European aircraft industry might be created is something else again. The Plowden Report asked unsuccessfully for a ministerial conference. Joucla dismisses both NATO and the EEC; NATO because France is not a member and because the organisation's interest lies only in military projects and the EEC because it excludes certain countries, is too rigid and is interested only in civil projects.[41] One is thrown back, it seems, on bodies like AICMA and on *ad hoc* progress. Meanwhile, the SORIS report on the European aerospace industry, produced for the EEC Commission in 1971, offers little comfort.

Understandably not well received in Britain, it concludes that,

> any close association between the EEC and UK aerospace
> industries would appear to be out of the queston until radical
> reorganisation has been carried out in the United Kingdom;
> otherwise a large proportion of the suggested support for the
> aerospace industry would inevitably go towards covering
> higher aerospace costs in the UK.[42]

This blunt observation, which has been challenged in Britain,[43] is
said to refer only to the airframe sector of the industry. For the rest,
having found that 'in the Community ... there is no aeroengine
industry worthy of the name', and that much the same could be said
of avionics, the report adds that 'very close cooperation with the
British engines branch is still necessary because this is the main
source from which the EEC aerospace industry can obtain the
know-how required to develop its own aero-engine industry'.

These are very provocative observations. Beteille had already
made full European collaboration in aviation sound rather alarming.
According to him it 'presupposes a resolute and irreversible will',
and he adds that 'once started, such cooperation cannot be halted
or limited without serious damage'.[44] As they stand these are views
likely to recommend themselves neither to politicians, nor, no less
important, to the industry itself. Nor, finally, is it any clearer from
the EEC Commission's 1972 proposals on the European aviation
industry how the creation, advocated there, of two or three 'European' airframe companies and a single aeroengine company might
actually be accomplished.[45] Equality in a unified organisation
intended to be permanent would obviously be even more of a
critical matter for each and every European company concerned
than equity in a once-off project, yet as shown in the next chapter,
this latter has itself been a highly sensitive issue.

The Space Field

In the space sector the scope for European industrial initiatives to
supplement or substitute for unreliable or non-existent governmental commitments has, in the nature of the technology, been
even more limited than in aviation. Here the experiences of ELDO[46]
and the European Space Research Organisation (ESRO) have been

predictably, but still instructively, different.[47] There was a false
neatness in Britain's putting forward, at both government and
company levels, the abandoned defence missile Blue Streak as the
first stage of a projected ELDO launcher, and an even more
beguiling simplicity in the parcelling out for a variety of motives, of
responsibility for the second and third stages to France and West
Germany respectively, with Italy, the Netherlands, Belgium and
Australia being allocated equally compartmentalised blocks of
responsibility. From the outset, national commitments fell far short
of the momentum called for by the programme's ambition. At the
initial Strasbourg Conference of January 1961, eleven countries
were represented and four sent observers; at the London Conference of October 1961, the numbers were down to eight and three
respectively, and when the Convention was signed in March 1962,
only seven countries remained. Worse followed, in that the Convention could not come into force until it had been ratified by
countries whose contributions together exceeded eighty-five per
cent of the total. This took until February 1964, and even then
Italy delayed for a further year. In the interim the ELDO organisation was damaged by having no legal personality, and in the later
opinion of the House of Commons Estimates Committee, though
not of ELDO itself, the delay 'was the biggest single factor in
upsetting the initial programme'.[48] It reflected, the Committee
thought, a straightforward lack of political will. Of all European
efforts in the technological field, ELDO is surely the one which
most inclines one to take the advice of Herodotus, to the effect that
since few things happen at the right time, and the rest do not
happen at all, it is left to the conscientious historian to correct such
irritating defects.

By contrast with ELDO's birth, the initiative which led to
ESRO sprang from the scientific community, in fact from scientists
connected with CERN, rather than from government, and although
when it came into existence in March 1964 it had been four years
evolving, ten of the original twelve countries remained. Nor did the
fact that the organisation was even then a little slow to get under
way have too harmful an effect.[49] It is also worth reflecting of
ESRO that, although the original initiative came from scientists,
the fact that it became a formal government commitment almost
certainly meant that more money was available in Britain, and no

doubt in the other member countries, for this branch of research than would otherwise have been the case.[50]

Already by 1964 both the costs, originally fixed at £70 millions, and the timing of ELDO's programme were seriously adrift, and the French call in 1965 for its replacement by a new and more advanced programme presented the organisation with its first major crisis. This was temporarily weathered, but in 1966 Britain precipitated a second crisis with her *aide-mémoires* of February and June. The first of these amounted to a long and forceful statement of the British Government's conviction that ELDO was engaged in developing an uncompetitive and obsolescent launcher, and that there was no obvious way of remedying the situation. ELDO thereupon advanced an alternative proposal, but after studying it the British Government issued their second *aide-mémoire*, together with a press statement which declared that 'For some time the Government has had serious doubts about whether or not it should continue to participate in the ELDO programme . . . the latest proposals . . . still do not constitute a sufficient basis for continuing United Kingdom participation'.[51]

Unilateral withdrawal by Britain was at this time legally impossible, and the Government quickly denied that it had ever been intended.[52] But officials, insisting that saying one doubted the wisdom of proceeding was not the same as proposing to withdraw, nevertheless admitted that the British move had been unfavourably interpreted by her partners. Whether the Government had been guilty of bad drafting or, as seemed the more likely, had made a shrewd diplomatic move, the outcome was agreement on a substantial downward revision of Britain's contribution to the organisation, from thirty-nine to twenty-seven per cent. At the same time ELDO's programme was modified and certain managerial changes put in hand.

When later the Causse Committee recommended an extension of ELDO's launcher programme, Britain, in the face of mounting costs, and given the presumed availability of American launchers, declined both to support an expanded ELDO programme and to meet the excess cost of completing the existing programme.[53] Later she announced a ceiling on her contribution of £11 millions as from 1969, finally asking to remain in the organisation only as an observer, though continuing to make Blue Streak available to

ELDO until its planned new Europa III launch vehicle could be completed. Quite naturally, she then came under increasing pressure from the countries left in ELDO to subcontract work on Blue Streak to Europe, so as to restrict to a minimum the cash flow into Britain.[54] Remembering that Britain had originally been the moving force behind ELDO, unless one believes that a competitive European launcher could be developed (competitive that is in the space-shuttle era of the late seventies), an honest description of Britain's withdrawal might be that it was 'economically sound but maybe politically not quite fair', and Britain's aerospace Minister himself conceded at the time that, notwithstanding her sound reasons for withdrawing, Britain perhaps did have something to live down in ELDO.[55] The whole unhappy programme certainly illustrates how frustrating inflexible arrangements can be while they obtain, and how damaging the consequences when they lapse.

ELDO was also designated as Europe's agency for studies of possible participation in the American post-Apollo programme. Britain agreed to participate in these studies and between the July and November 1970 meetings of the European Space Conference, the Lefèvre Mission to the United States investigated the political prospects for participation. At the November meeting the British Government refused unequivocally to join in a $35 millions programme 'described as being for the purpose of post-Apollo studies'. To have taken any other view would, in the Aerospace Minister's opinion, have been 'stark staring round the bend'. He explained that

> It was not . . . until a good deal of hard cross-examination that it appeared that by far the greater part of the $35 million was, in fact, to be directed to the launcher programme which we had made perfectly clear in July we were not prepared to enter . . . this is not the way in which we believe we could enhance and advance the collaborative proposals and projects.[56]

Britain's attitude on the post-Apollo questions can be seen as in marked contrast to her conduct in the negotiations over Intelsat. Here, it was officially admitted, a special problem for Britain was that

> tactically, and on some important points of substance, we had

to operate in as close concert as possible with Europeans ...
during the period of the 'approach to Europe' and in the EEC
negotiation, it was necessary for the United Kingdom to
avoid, without harming our basic Intelstat interests, getting
out of line with our European partners.[57]

The British had come in the late sixties to hope that the way
forward in space for Europe would prove to be through a minimum
common programme funded by all states, with an *à la carte*
approach for everything else. The principle underlying this had
been canvassed by Mr Wedgwood Benn when Minister of Technology:

> We also had to get across the idea that European countries
> engaged in space should not all be compelled to take the same
> line. We thought that there should be a self-selective approach
> ... One of the great reasons for the failure of ... discussions in
> the past was that Cabinets commit their representatives ...
> before they go and the result is that there is no flexibility in
> discussion.[58]

The National Industrial Space Committee's memorandum to the
House of Commons Science Committee in 1971 contained a more
specific form of this idea, providing for a minimum common funding for all projects, the opportunity for members to allocate the bulk
of their contribution at will, and the guarantee of a reasonable
return through contracts. BAC's memorandum to the same Committee was also a development on this theme.[59] It made the basic
points that true economies depended on scale and on specialisation,
and that success itself depended on Governments having 'whole-
hearted mutual and complementary interest in the projects'. The
first of these had not, BAC thought, been achieved in the space
field, and the second seemed hardly to be a practical proposition
given the number of governments involved. New and more flexible
rules were therefore needed and, BAC added succinctly: 'If governments can resolve their problems, then industry can satisfactorily
undertake the development, as has already been demonstrated.'

Some 150 firms interested in space, drawn from nine European
countries, have since 1961 formed a general space lobby through
the EUROSPACE organisation, but the onus of commitment has

unavoidably continued to lie with governments. Since 1968, and especially after the disastrous November 1970 meeting of the European Space Conference, they have been sharply divided on at least three major issues, namely whether to construct a new European launcher or to rely on the Americans to make theirs available, the scope of European participation in the American post-Apollo programme and the unification and financial strengthening of the existing European space programmes. By the autumn of 1972 the second issue had faded slightly, the United States having lost much of her earlier apparent enthusiasm for European participation in the post-Apollo programme, or at least in the technically most rewarding parts of it.[60] For this there were several reasons, one being the low American regard for European technical and managerial competence in this field. But the changed American attitude served only to underline the disagreements in ELDO, disagreements which it was fairly said at this time provided 'an astringent counter-point to the Paris summit'.[61] Cairns was not alone in concluding that intra-European cooperation in space research and technology was on the decline, though for this he blamed the new European and global concern with the environment as much as the troubles within the existing space programmes.[62]

Europe's difficulties in agreeing a space strategy seem in fact to be instructively different from the sorts of problem encountered in arranging other schemes of technological collaboration. In this case there appears to have been a more than usually genuine recognition of the desirability of common action, with markedly fewer of the commercial, institutional and other internal obstacles which have so often frustrated collaboration in other sectors. The particular difficulty in this instance has been the need to base common action squarely on an appreciation of the probable development of American space technology, and even more important, on assumptions about American political and commercial attitudes towards Europe in the late seventies and eighties. To put the matter simply, collaboration in other sectors is for the European nations first and foremost a game amongst themselves, and then as it were a game against nature; in the case of space collaboration there is also a game against the Americans to be played. The French and British positions may be taken as polar opposites. The French insist that America cannot be relied upon to provide launch facilities for European satellites which have a technological, as opposed to a scientific, objective. The British are prepared to countenance such dependence. Taking the most important type of technological applications satellite, the communications satellite, the international political and commercial significance of this may well be profound. Now, even if the Americans chose to forgo any political advantages which might fall to them should Europe not provide herself with a launch capability, it nevertheless seems likely that they would seek as satisfactory as possible a commercial return on their enormous investments in space. And in addition to the commercial interests of the US Government there would presumably be a vigorous American lobby with its own commercial interests in space. The problem therefore reduces itself so far as Europe is concerned to deciding whether to accept the political risk of dependence on the Americans, and within this, to deciding how the surcharge likely to be levied directly or indirectly by the Americans would compare with the cost of a European launcher.

It has sometimes been suggested that development by the United States of the shuttle, effectively a re-usable launcher, should settle this question for Europe, on the grounds that the best Europe could then hope to accomplish would be the possession by the end of the seventies of a technology which the Americans would by that time be in a position to discard. That is: 'Like it or not, Europe is going to have to come to terms with the United States.'[63] But there may be a fallacy here. If the essential objective were the development of the technology itself, then naturally there would be little point in Europe simply following the United States a decade or more behind. But here the technology is only a means to an end, the end is the orbiting of satellites, and in satellite technology Europe has managed to maintain a respectable performance. Furthermore, one study has suggested that the economic advantage of the space shuttle may not, in its early years, be as great as has sometimes been believed.[64]

There is evidently a close parallel between the British and French positions on nuclear weapons and on launchers, France's nuclear weapon being independent in a sense that Britain's is not. But by comparison with the burden France has borne in developing her nuclear weapon, Britain has hardly been put at a disadvantage by her dependence on the United States. The two cases differ in that the issues in the case of nuclear weapons are wholly political, whereas in the case of launchers they are at least as much commercial, and the United States may be prepared to look for commercial profits where she would not try to score political points. Of course, this question may never be fully resolved, in that American attitudes may well be different from what they would otherwise be if a successful launcher were developed in Europe. To this extent, M. Pompidou and Herr Brandt were taking out an insurance policy in January 1973 in deciding provisionally to develop the L-3S, an essentially French launch vehicle expected to cost only some two thirds of ELDO's Europa III proposal. An immediate requirement at this time, so far as the French and German governments were concerned, was the guarantee of a launch vehicle for their joint satellite Symphonie, given the dubious prospects of ELDO's Europa II and III and the uncertainty of an American launcher for non-scientific versions of this satellite. But this was an insurance policy moreover from which, if it were brought to fruition, Britain, though not a participant, could also hope indirectly to benefit, in that it might help further to ensure the indefinite availability of American launchers, and their availability at fair prices.[65]

Returning finally from ELDO to ESRO, it is not really so strange that the two European space organisations, established at almost the same time, should have had such different careers. They had after all ended up with different memberships, there was no provision that the one would launch the other's satellites, and, in short, they were given virtually no mutual interests. Commercial considerations were then far from centre stage, and it has not inaccurately been said of this phase that 'the main problem of space policy in Europe ... was that we all thought of hardware first'.[66]

The problem of securing commitment was not seriously encountered by ESRO until the organisation moved on from purely scientific objectives to the study of applications satellites. Previously, full governmental support had been forthcoming for all projects, though this was not strictly necessary under the Convention. The ESRO secretariat itself felt that such support for projects from which a country could expect little return was 'the embodiment of cooperation, the willingness to "give" and "take" for the sake of overall European progress'.[67] But even ESRO sometimes felt itself to be a political football as member states sought to pressurize each other through it. Especially after Britain's withdrawal from ELDO, French retaliation, with some support from other ELDO members, took the form of stalling on ESRO's Applications Satellite Programme, and even of holding out the threat of a French withdrawal from ESRO, so that 'only with difficulty' was a compromise programme arranged for 1971.[68] In spite of these difficulties, however, the ESRO Council did during 1971 reach substantial agreement on an Applications Satellite Programme, Europe's first well-defined long-term satellite programme. Under this agreement Britain, France, West Germany and Italy agreed to support all applications programmes, with the smaller countries being granted a greater freedom in their contributions.[69]

It was said by one commentator of this achievement that the ESRO Council had found 'a sophisticated method of bypassing' the normal decision-making machinery for European space policies.[70] On the other hand, organisational retrenchment became essential, and ESRO continued into 1973 to be affected by the uncertainty surrounding Europe's post-Apollo involvement with the United States, the organisation having commissioned studies from each of three European space consortia on the sortie module, or space laboratory, for the post-Apollo programme.[71] All in all the European nations had still not really gone very far toward realising the dream of ESRO's former Director-General, Professor Bondi. In a very touching article in 1969 he had pointed out that, whereas the United States spent three and sixpence a head per week on space, ESRO received only a halfpenny per head of the European population.[72] He hoped, he said, for three farthings, 'but then I am ambitious'. All commitments are relative.

The Nuclear Sector

Given the extent of Anglo-French aerospace collaboration, and the fact that theirs have been the two largest, publicly supported, civil nuclear power programmes in Western Europe, it is a remarkable commentary on the status of collaboration that the two countries have collaborated so little in the nuclear sector. Since both their programmes were based until the late sixties on the same technology, gas-graphite reactors, and since both met strong commercial pressure from the alternative American technology of light water reactors (the PWR and BWR), the lack of a joint approach appears still more curious. There were a variety of joint studies and experiments between the British AEA and the French CEA but little came of them, despite such remarks as that by M. Maurice Schumann, as French Minister of Scientific Research, to the effect that mutual cooperation opened the way to the survival of both the British and the French nuclear industries.[73]

Britain had her initial crisis of confidence in gas graphite technology a little before France, but with a developed version, the AGR, of her basic magnox reactor, felt able in 1965 to justify proceeding with the type. France by contrast experimented rather unsuccessfully with heavy-water reactor technology, but did not develop an advanced magnox comparable with the AGR. With magnox obsolescent by the mid-sixties, the immediate alternatives before both countries were therefore American light water reactors or the British AGR, and it is easy to believe that Britain 'leaned over backwards to offer reactor cooperation without offending French susceptibilities on British designs',[74] but with the passing of General de Gaulle, the French electricity authority, EDF, insisted on switching to the American type.

If, from the point of view of nuclear technology, an Anglo-French joint approach had most to recommend it at the governmental level, at the commercial level the development of intercompany links in Europe has proceeded apace in recent years. Indeed, the *Economist* referred somewhat scathingly in 1971 to a European 'haze of cooperative goodwill'.[75] By then the European operations of the American General Electric and Westinghouse companies had for some six years and more been highly successful in consolidating the place of the light water reactor, though there had been some determined resistance, especially that by the French Government to the Westinghouse takeover of the Jeumont Schneider Company.[76] It had thus been in a market dominated by American-developed light-water reactors that British companies had had to work in the late sixties – unsuccessfully as it turned out – to promote the AGR, Britain's APC consortium for example, forming links with BBC (West Germany) and SOCIA (France), and the TNPG consortium with Belgonucleare (Belgium) and SNAM-Progetti (Italy). These industrial links may be seen in part as designed to compensate for the fact that European nuclear R & D had been, and still remained, very nationalistic. The highly simplified table below brings this point out.

Reactor	Countries particularly interested	
Gas cooled, graphite moderated	Britain	France
Gas cooled, heavy water moderated	West Germany	France
Light water cooled, light water moderated	West Germany (US licensees)	Sweden
Light water cooled, heavy water moderated	Britain	Italy
Heavy water cooled, heavy water moderated	West Germany	Sweden
Organic liquid cooled, heavy water moderated	Euratom	Italy
High temperature reactors	West Germany	ENEA (Britain)
Sodium fast breeder	Britain	France
	The West Germany – Benelux consortium	Italy

This nationalistic approach has led almost inevitably to considerable duplication. The most blatant instance of this, as is well known, has occurred in the European development of fast breeder reactors, the British, French and West German-Benelux programmes all being based on sodium cooling. Albonetti in 1972 put British expenditure already incurred on this type of reactor at $300 millions, French expenditure at $350 millions, with a further $150 millions necessary to complete the Phénix industrial prototype, and the planned West German-Benelux expenditure at $180 millions up to 1969. In addition, Albonetti gives Italian expenditure leading to the PEC fast reactor facility at $55 millions up to 1971, and points out that between 1962 and 1967, when this much criticised assistance was halted, Euratom contributed $52, $28 and $9 millions respectively to the French, West German and Italian programmes, only Italy, the country with most to gain, responding positively to EEC Commission proposals for coordination.[77]

This emphasis wherever possible on national independence had also extended to commercial construction. Here, for example, the award by Dutch authorities of the contract for the Tihange power station to KWU (Germany), which meant passing over a joint offer from Neratoom (Netherlands) and Westinghouse, was hailed as the first major break with the policy followed by each European country of favouring its own industry, though even here KWU had in advance guaranteed some seventy-six per cent of the work to Dutch subcontractors.[78] Despite this, and KWU's subsequent European successes, it may take some time for Epstein[79] to be proved right. 'The economics of developing and producing heavy electrical equipment', she argues, 'will eventually transcend the problems of national pride as manifested in public procurement policies'.

To get the European picture in wholly fair perspective, it needs to be pointed out that the pattern of national independence has been supplemented at the margin by some limited international contact or collaboration, for example between France and Spain on magnox, France and West Germany on gas-cooled heavy water reactors, and France and Belgium, and Britain and Belgium on different types of light water reactor. In view of the American dominance in the latter reactor, it is perhaps particularly surprising that there was not more European collaboration on the type, especially when Euratom itself spent some $60 millions on them in its first decade.

The two most important European collaborative ventures in reactor development have undoubtedly been the European Nuclear Energy Agency's (ENEA) high temperature reactor project DRAGON, and the programme involving Interatom (West Germany; seventy per cent), Belgonucleare and Neratoom (fifteen per cent each) in the development of the sodium cooled fast breeder. DRAGON is an intergovernmental project, a much less common collaborative form in the nuclear sector than in the aerospace field. For this there seem to be several reasons, including Euratom's difficulties and the absence of joint military requirements. There are also the two reasons implied by Lord Sherfield, an ex-chairman of the AEA. Like Mr Healey in regard to aerospace collaboration, Lord Sherfield has said of the number of collaborating parties in intergovernmental nuclear projects 'the fewer, the better', and he has added of the timing 'the earlier, the easier'.[80]

Two potentially important industrial agreements in the late sixties were those between TNGP, Belgonucleare, SNAM-

Progetti and GHN (West Germany), creating Inter Nuclear under Belgian law, with a view to the commercial exploitation of the high temperature reactor; and between the first three of these companies and ASEA-Atom (Sweden), Brown Boveri-Krupp (West Germany), Brown Boveri and others (Switzerland) and Neratoom, for a joint study of the prospects of the gas-cooled fast breeder reactor.[81] In 1970, complementing the DRAGON agreement, a group of major European electricity undertakings, including Britain's CEGB, France's EDF and West German utilities, formed Euro HKG to arrange an exchange of high temperature reactor views and experience with the manufacturing companies. Moves of the kind which led to Inter Nuclear and Euro HKG had for some time seemed very necessary if the American GGA company were to be prevented from enjoying the same sort of success in Europe with high temperature reactors as General Electric and Westinghouse had earlier had with light water ones;[82] hence also the EEC Commission's concern from the outset to get Euro HKG to decide on a common specification for the high temperature reactor.

Sir Stanley Brown, the chairman of the CEGB, stressed at the time the importance of utilities, as opposed to governments or manufacturing companies, in creating a European nuclear community, and apart from Euro HKG, utilities do appear to have begun to act more in concert on nuclear questions. Thus an agreement was reached in 1971 between EDF (France), RWE (West Germany) and ENEL (Italy) on the formation of joint subsidiaries to build the first commercial reactors based on the French and German-Benelux fast reactor prototypes, and in 1972 the Gas Breeder Reactor Association decided to offer associate membership to utilities.[83]

The most exciting European industrial agreement during this period was, by general acclaim, that reached between TNPG of Britain and KWU of West Germany in July 1971, one of seven collaborative pacts concluded simultaneously, and involving also Interatom, Belgonucleare, Agip Nucleare (Italy), Neratoom, BNFL (Britain), and the West German Karlsruhe organisation. Only France of the Community's nuclear countries remained unrepresented in these interlinking compacts, and this in spite of KWU's expressed desire for a French partner, and in spite of Franco-West German interministerial discussions on the subject.[84]

KWU were by now a major force in the European nuclear industry, responsible for the nuclear interests of the major West German companies AEG and Siemens, whose own nuclear strength had been established with the initial assistance of American General Electric (BWR) and Westinghouse (PWR) licenses respectively. KWU and TNPG had before this collaborated on tenders in third countries and between them were now in a position to offer to customers virtually every type of reactor. Their most urgent objective had obviously to be that of staying on competitive terms with the American companies, but particularly exciting possibilities were also thought to have been created by the link with respect to the commercial exploitation of the fast reactor. TNPG had by this time taken over responsibility for the British prototype of this reactor, and Interatom, like KWU partly owned by Siemens, were responsible for the West German-Benelux one. Collaboration between these two projects, and with the similar French one, had long been advocated by spokesmen of many European interests, but it had consistently proved impossible to provide for this at government level, partly because of the different development states reached by the three projects. KWU and TNPG following their compact claimed to have government approval for collaboration, but there were known still to be many complications. From the British point of view two in particular stemmed from the chronic uncertainties surrounding both the overall structure of the country's nuclear industry and the content of the immediate nuclear power programme. The (unpublished) Vintner Report, completed for the Government in 1972, did not finally resolve these latter two questions.

As regards reactors, then, there has been a gathering momentum of European collaboration through links forged primarily by private industry. With respect to the nuclear fuel cycle there has been some parallel activity, except that here the commitment has mostly needed still to be governmental. Thus, in 1969 governmental and industrial interests from eight countries formed a company, SFU, to exploit a new process for one part of this cycle. Of greater moment, in October 1971 Britain, France and West Germany formed a new joint company, United Reprocessors, pooling their fuel reprocessing capacity so as to keep European capacity in line with demand. In effect this fifteen-year agreement committed the three governments to utilising the existing British and French plants to the full before proceeding later to construct a further plant in Germany, ownership of the plants themselves remaining in national hands. Until this agreement the one example of European cooperation in reprocessing had been ENEA's Eurochemic, created as an international company by twelve European countries in 1957, with Spain joining in 1959. As Albonetti says, Eurochemic was first mooted at a time when a European enrichment plant was also being discussed, and this latter initiative having collapsed, 'one of the main political reasons underlying the creation of Eurochemic ... ceased to exist'. Commercially also, Eurochemic proved to be a disappointment, because, following a fifty per cent escalation in capital cost, it found itself faced with a wholly inadequate demand for its services, as well as with cost undercutting by Britain.

The prime example of European collaboration in the nuclear fuel cycle is, of course, the tripartite centrifuge project started in 1968–9 by Britain, West Germany and the Netherlands.[85] The reprocessing pact has been said to differ from this in that it is more a producers' than a developers' agreement, the technology being relatively straightforward. Furthermore, there is no security angle to reprocessing, and overcapacity is already a reality. The possibility of another treaty, on plutonium fabrication, has also been canvassed, to 'weld Europe's nuclear nations into a common pool of nuclear fuel services', and there has already been some European collaboration on this.[86]

Full integration of nuclear fuel services in Europe remains a long-term prospect. For the moment, the tripartite centrifuge agreement has, with good reason, been described as 'probably the most important development in European technological cooperation', and important politically no less than technologically and commercially.[87] The rapidly growing European and world demand for enriched uranium, and the wide and deep European desire for independence from the United States in this critical resource, meant that, unusually, in this case there was from the beginning no real problem of securing adequate public funds for what three countries in Europe alone regarded as a highly promising technology. But in part precisely because this, as the British Minister of Technology pointed out when it was undertaken, was the first European collaborative project with a market virtually guaranteed in advance, its importance ensured that there would be long and detailed negotiations over the proper organisational and commercial way of proceeding. There were also other complications, especially the problems concerning the comparative standing of the three countries' earlier independent work with centrifuges. And there was the question of competition from the other proved method of enrichment, diffusion, and its firm supporters, the French.

The French had earlier tried unsuccessfully to have their own Pierrelatte diffusion plant 'Europeanised', and they continued at the highest political level thereafter to press the advantages of diffusion, so that there developed some degree of mistrust between the sincerely held British and French points of view. The French received some reward for their persistence in February 1972, when it was announced that public and private organisations from the Community countries and Britain had set up a joint study project on diffusion technology, but even then the British, Dutch and West German participants were the same ones as were developing the centrifuge, and it was assumed that they viewed the new exercise as a means of finally convincing the French as to the centrifuge's economic advantage over diffusion.[88] Apart from these reservations by the French, the Italians and Belgians were also known to be concerned at their exclusion from the centrifuge agreement, and the EEC Commission, long a fervent proponent of a Community-owned plant of whatever type, itself required to be satisfied that the tripartite agreement did not infringe the Euratom treaty.

Another sensitive aspect of this collaborative project has been its potential military dimension. Some observers have been convinced that joint development of the centrifuge will accelerate its introduction, simplify and cheapen the process of enrichment to military grade uranium and thereby facilitate the spread of H-bombs. Past experience with other technical collaborative projects has made them fear that decisions will be made on purely technological grounds, and some of them have felt that Britain has a special responsibility.[89] For others, such arguments are specious; plutonium for A-bombs is in any case increasingly easily obtainable, and it is 'better that this advance in the nuclear technology of Germany should be achieved in a consortium with Britain and Holland than that it should be achieved in German industry internally'.[90] Leonard Beaton was an especially severe critic of this project and he sought to put it in overall European context, contending that of all the arguments in favour of it

> the European ones are the worst. International collaboration can be as fruitful a source of difficulty and dispute as of amity . . . a politically sensitive European Collaborative arrangement without France has obvious disadvantages . . . British entry into the European communities, if desirable, will not be achieved by indiscriminate agreements with individual countries which are already members.[91]

Whether or not Beaton turns out to be right, the tripartite project belongs in a quite different category from Anglo-French collaboration on nuclear weapons. Whatever one's views as to the wisdom or desirability of the latter, it, and even more a wider European collaboration on nuclear weapons, would obviously signify an unprecedented commitment to technological collaboration. David Owen, for example, a junior minister in Britain's last Labour Government, makes just this point. Convinced that Europe should not pursue 'the fanciful charisma of an expensive and probably unobtainable total nuclear independence' he argues that 'The overriding need is to develop a greater European identity within NATO. Such an identity will not be developed merely by collaborating over mundane military hardware, but it might be attained through collaboration on the central issue of nuclear deterrence'.[92]

In the late sixties discussion of this issue was catalysed by two factors in particular, one mainly political and the other more technical and economic. The first was the reference by Edward Heath in the Godkin Lectures of 1967 to an Anglo-French nuclear force held 'in trusteeship for Europe', a hint which was thought to be of the greatest significance when in 1970 Mr Heath became Prime Minister and elaborated slightly on his proposal: 'My conception has been that the non-nuclear countries of Europe could join with Britain and France in a Consultative Committee which would have exactly the same relationship to the joint Anglo-French deterrent as the so-called McNamara Committee has to the US deterrent.'[93] The idea was naturally taken very seriously in Britain, and there was a definite French response,[94] but Mr Heath had not linked his proposal to British membership of the EEC and in spite of another reference to the possibility by the Defence Secretary at the 1972

Conservative Conference, no positive step really seemed likely to result, at least for some years.[95]

The second catalysing factor, acting on the first, is what Pierre has called the 'inherent logic' of collaboration on nuclear weapons between Britain and France. His conclusion is that 'since existing strengths and weaknesses are roughly complementary, the technical basis for an agreement on collaboration undoubtedly does exist'. But he also adds that political requirements are paramount, and among the obstacles he cites are the need to extend any agreement to include targeting, deployment, and therefore general policy, the divergent views of the two countries on the Atlantic Alliance, the difficulties of disentangling the Anglo-American nuclear agreements if the United States offered objection and the likely hostility of West Germany to any Anglo-French nuclear weapon coordination.[96]

The really fundamental political difficulty in the way of Anglo-French nuclear weapon collaboration is generally held to be the uncompromising French view that 'The decision to employ nuclear forces can be made only by a single nation'.[97] These are the words of M. Debré, French Defence Minister, and he has also said that 'As for cooperation between Britain and France in the nuclear field, we know the impossibility of going beyond mere words'. This attitude has remained sufficient of a barrier for there to have been relatively little public study of the equations relating costs, strategic doctrine and the future utility of the two nuclear forces. However, one suspects that the real difficulties are by no means all summed up in the person of M. Debré or in the defence policy he has come to represent. It may instead be that so long as this obstacle is so evident the existence of others can conveniently be overlooked. Meanwhile, Britain has found herself faced with the questions of whether and how to provide for the technical updating of her deterrent, and the United States with the reciprocal questions of whether and how to help her.[98] To make the argument virtually circular, American willingness once more to assist Britain could be construed as decreasing still further any chances of Anglo-French cooperation.[99]

Those with suspicions of an 'Anglo-French', or even a 'European' nuclear weapon, whether on grounds of cost, utility, or because they fear its destabilizing influence, will find Mr George Thomson's conclusion a reasonable one: 'I do not myself believe that the question of an Anglo-French nuclear deterrent can or ought to become a real issue for some years.'[100]

They will also agree with Herr Barzel that, if ever Europe is to possess a nuclear weapon potential, then it can be 'only at the end of the integration process. It is not a suitable instrument for initiating or accelerating integration'.[101] François Duchêne, director of the Institute for Strategic Studies, makes the point even more strongly. The idea of a European nuclear force has, he feels, received too much attention, and nuclear deterrents 'mark a potential divide, not a link, in the European Community'.[102]

The Case of Computers

In both the aerospace and nuclear sectors it has usually been fairly clear when a European commitment was an available option, and it has also normally been possible to foresee broadly what it would require and entail. In the event, governments have sometimes committed themselves, sometimes eschewed collaborative opportunities, and in any case have felt free to vacillate and play politics. By contrast, in the computer sector identification of the possible dimensions of a 'European solution' or 'solutions' has taken longer, and the issue of governmental commitment to such solutions has consequently not arisen quite as distinctly. In its absence government policies have unsurprisingly been singularly nationalistic. In the words of a senior British civil servant, 'The problem has been, frankly, in this field to produce results rather than good intentions or goodwill', and in those of an interested party, AEG-Telefunken (West Germany), 'Cooperation . . . is necessary and desirable . . . However, no answer has been found yet as to how such a cooperation should be implemented'.[103]

It is not as if there were no incentives. Quite the reverse, since the American challenge has here already amounted largely to a conquest, IBM and the other major American companies taking some eighty to eighty-five per cent of the European market.[104] The adjective 'humiliating' used by one commentator[105] perfectly reflects the especially sensitive European reaction in this case, European governments having mostly settled for propping up their own industries as best they have been able by providing funds, promoting mergers, and buying preferentially. In Britain, market forces and financial encouragement by government eventually produced ICL, Europe's strongest group, after a series of mergers and takeovers during the sixties. In France, the Government, having failed in 1964 to prevent Machines Bull falling under American control, thereupon drew up Plan Calcul to reorganise and develop the French industry, a new company CII emerging, backed by public funds. In West Germany too, government funds were eventually made available to encourage rationalisation.

There were some attempts to find a basis for cross-national groupings. Bull, Olivetti (Italy), Siemens, ICT (Britain) and English Electric were all involved in an abortive attempt in the early sixties. In the mid-sixties talks between ICT and CITEC (France), and others which might have led to two Anglo-West German groups, all proved inconclusive. In 1969 the Eurodata consortium, formed after 'considerable effort' by ICL, CII, Philips (Netherlands), AEG-Telefunken, Saab and Olivetti, tendered for an ESRO computer requirement. Its offer was some twenty per cent above IBM's and, although ESRO officials were prepared to accept it because of its significance for the future of the European computer industry, the proposal received only a simple majority and not the required two-thirds majority in the ESRO council, the West German Government, lobbied by Siemens, voting against it despite AEG-Telefunken's involvement. The venture thereupon collapsed in 'international disarray'. This was probably an important chance lost. Another is thought to have occurred at the time of Honeywell's takeover of GE-Bull. ICL and CII were interested on that occasion in the French Government preventing the takeover and instead allowing the two European firms to take GE-Bull over jointly, the British Government putting up some of the funds. This proposal seems to have been a casualty of the uncertainties produced by the British General Election of 1970.[106]

If the Eurodata and GE-Bull cases were two real opportunities missed, the situation opened up by the Aigrain Committee's proposal for computers was less of one. The Committee advocated the construction of a giant European computer and their plan was studied by representatives of both industry and government but, as ICL explained later, 'after much detailed examination of the possibilities, it was decided that a basis for collaboration in the development of a large European computer system did not exist'.

In evidence to the Commons Science Committee Mr Corfield, the responsible British Minister, left no doubt that he would for his part have wanted a more precise definition of objectives before committing public money.[107] The lessons drawn from these three cases by a committee of European parliamentarians are first, 'the necessity of deliberate efforts to work for common European standards'; second, that 'well-meaning *ad hoc* international projects' are not likely to succeed while governments continue to offer support only on a national basis; third, that 'a high level of political understanding between the key governments . . . is a precondition' of policy; and finally, that 'bringing six computer companies together in a political forum is the least likely way of encouraging two or three of them to merge'.[108]

More limited attempts have continued at the industrial level, but they have also involved American interests. Thus ICL and CII joined with CDC of America to form Multinational Data, whose immediate objectives were stated to centre on standardisation rather than on research coordination. But as a catalyst of European collaboration, though not apparently commercially, this in turn seemed to founder,[109] CII coming to a separate agreement with CDC, and more important still, in January 1972 joining also with Siemens and Philips in what was regarded as the most determined collaborative effort to date. This was an initiative which caused some definite concern in Britain because ICL were outside the new grouping.[110]

ICL had previously insisted not only that they wanted a European solution to American dominance, but that they had taken the lead in pursuing it. They saw that European political agreement on the matter was essential, but it was no less essential, they felt, that industry take the initiative.[111] They would have liked a 'small but high-powered European computer Secretariat under a strong Director', and also European consortia. Their part in the attempts at collaboration already mentioned, talks with still other potential partners, such as Nixdorf (West Germany), and links with CII and Philips in pursuit of a contract at the new Paris airport, all go some way towards bearing out the company's interest in collaboration. They were also aware that their comparative size made possible European partners almost as suspicious of them as of IBM:

We must be very careful not necessarily to think that this

problem is going to be solved by a series of mergers . . . in a sense, ICL is too big . . . the objective must be for Governments, both individually and collectively, to order more computers and to order them in a more competent manner.[112]

However, some commentators have speculated that in playing from strength ICL may have tended to overplay their hand, perhaps refusing to contemplate any loss of control in a joint venture. There is some evidence of this in that ICL believed that the French Government recognised 'that some arrangement with Britain in the form of ICL is a fundamental'. 'Any effort of unification', the company insisted, 'must centre around ICL'.[113] Similarly their response, in part, to the Siemens-Philips-CII link was that it would 'undoubtedly make it easier for the companies concerned to discuss further cooperation with ICL on equal terms in terms of size and technological capability'. This apart, ICL seem to have regarded the link-up between these three companies as of only marginal significance so far as Europe's overall position in computers was concerned,[114] and subsequently they gave evidence of a more international than European outlook, contemplating for instance a merger with Burroughs or Univac of the United States, or collaboration with the Japanese industry.[115] An eventual merger with European companies was also not a condition of the Government's loan to the company in July 1972, though in announcing it the Minister for Industrial Development repeated that such an arrangement must, in the view of both ICL and the Government, make sense.

To castigate ICL's efforts to achieve a rationalized European computer industry would, without full details of the successive negotiations, be unfair, since it is likely that, if ICL's efforts could have been more positive, then so also might those of some of the other European companies. The fact remains that, chauvinism being particularly intense in this case, it has not been easy for European governments to come to terms with the kind of collaborative arrangement in which ICL would have a role appropriate to their strength. But it is not obviously significant that, excluding the Aigrain and ESRO schemes, there has been no 'European' body to which the various companies might have looked for guidance or direction. The tougher attitude on the part of the EEC Commission to national policies of preference and support for computers, as foreshadowed by one of its senior officials in January 1973,[116] is of course directly in line with the Commission's efforts to open up public procurement in Europe. Here again, however, the conclusion must be that such exhortation, while no doubt necessary and worthy, is not a sufficient condition of action. The Commission cannot substitute for political and commercial will, and that, manifestly, in this sector above all, has been lacking.

Conclusion

It can easily be seen therefore that the problem of generating a commitment to collaborative technological projects within Europe is generally (aerospace) a severe and sometimes (computers) an insurmountable one. If one were looking for a final extreme example, what more natural one than the Channel Tunnel? Drilling towards this end had started no less than eighty-five years before a joint Anglo-French working party decided in 1963 in favour of twin rail tunnels. At the time of writing the cost is put at £366 millions, a figure which would no doubt climb to £1,000 millions or more in practice. France is keener on the project than Britain, for obvious commercial reasons, but it is interesting that the venture still tends to be thought of as a 'Channel Tunnel' rather than as a 'European Link'. There is after all no longer any reason on security grounds for excluding other governments, and there are some valid commercial and political grounds for encouraging their participation if, that is, the project goes ahead.

And having mentioned the Tunnel, somewhat dubiously, in this brief review of European commitment to technological collaboration, one may profitably conclude with sharply contrasting quotations from editorials published in *The Times* in 1967 and 1972 respectively, one dealing with British support for CERN's proposed new particle accelerator, the other with British support for the Tunnel. To be fair to *The Times*, these are very different propositions, and the cost to Britain of the one might be of the order of ten times and more that of the other. But the CERN project itself is not cheap – its cost was then put at £130 millions – and the editorials did highlight a feature which in the past has greatly influenced British commitment to European technological collaboration. Conceding that the national case for British membership of the new CERN project was inadequate, and that the scientific case on a world scale was open to question, *The Times* in 1967 still concluded that: 'If Britain means business in Europe, this is one way to show it. [Our answer] should be one of faith in Europe.'[117]

Writing of the Tunnel in 1972, the newspaper numbered it among the 'grandiose and technically exciting' projects which the country should have learned to treat very cautiously, as one whose unsoundness might be revealed only as costs increased and commitment inexorably hardened. *The Times* this time concluded that: 'With Britain's entry into Europe now assured, there is no longer a need to engage in projects of this kind to make a political gesture, nor to persist in them for fear of displeasing the French.'[118]

The contrast between these two quotations no doubt exaggerates the historical importance of one factor in commitment, but there is a very fundamental fact which both of them bring out, namely that such commitment has been seen as overwhelmingly a matter of national calculation and self interest.

V   The Process of Collaboration

Questions of Organisation: Aviation

European technological collaboration has been wrapped in many different institutional forms, public, private and mixed. The particular organisational framework within which it comes to be conducted, apart from being a monument to the problems encountered in generating commitment, seems likely itself to be potentially the source of new ones, and the topic is probably worth more study than it has so far received. As regards scientific collaboration, as a recent Unesco report says: 'The method resorted to in the process of selection, management, support and control of European schemes . . . is generally the crude one of trial and error.'[1]

And in the sphere of technology, a recent British White Paper sums up one of the major difficulties: 'Collaborative projects . . . call for complex administrative machinery and involve delays and frustrations which would be quite unacceptable in pursuit of normal commercial procurement.'[2]

Scale, organisation and approach all naturally depend upon whether the project is primarily political, commercial, or scientific, and it has been said that: 'In general, firm to firm approaches can more readily generate across-frontier projects than can governments, they act more quickly and decisively, but have less financial stability and cannot undertake major risks.'[3]

A project's characteristics will obviously affect the choice of organisational arrangement, but in inter-governmental projects one would usually expect the wishes of the procurement authorities to be decisive. In all cases there seems every reason to believe that there is indeed 'a "know-how" of collaboration, particularly international collaboration'.[4]

Different authors distinguish different numbers of collaborative arrangements in advanced technology, and it has pointedly been said of all of them, except the purely private, that they inevitably involve governments in different degrees of loss of sovereignty.[5] Layton outlines three main types of arrangement. Of the first, an international group of subcontractors working to a prime contractor, he says that its great advantage is that, provided the contract system is properly devised, 'responsibility can be clearly delegated down the line and disciplines imposed'. He believes that a second type, the international consortium, can be effective where competitive pressures are strong, and he cites the European airbus project as an example, but costly where they are so weak as to allow members to sub-maximise. Such consortia he regards as in any case suitable only for one-off projects. Layton recalls that a third type, joint subsidiaries, have proliferated in the chemical, oil and other industries, but in aerospace have had to be learned anew in the evolution from Concorde through Jaguar to the MRCA. He thinks even the joint subsidiary limited in scope, partly because the common interest can disappear, partly because of potential management disagreements, and partly because its impermanence is wasteful.[6] An experienced practitioner of collaboration has been still more explicit. A single contracting agency is, according to this authority, 'highly desirable', but is subject to 'industrial greed and a general chauvinism' which can mean that some companies are put at a disadvantage; joint companies help but do not resolve the basic questions concerning responsibility, liability, profit and loss: 'These have to be negotiated . . . whatever the legal machinery.'[7]

These quotations do more than hint that organisational questions can be vital ones, and in the light of them this chapter will briefly examine the experiences of the aviation industry, where perhaps most has been learned, of the space sector, where ELDO exemplifies so many of Europe's problems, and of the nuclear community, where familiarity with collaboration is least, yet still instructive.

Of the early collaborative aircraft projects, Transall was managed by a joint working committee of the French and West German companies concerned, VFW-Fokker acting as overall production manager, while the Atlantique was built by a consortium consisting of some nine companies from four (later five) European countries, with Breguet having development and management responsibility, through the SECBAT company set up by the collaborating companies. At the government level both projects, like the earlier Noratlas, were managed by Steering Committees. The engine chosen for both Atlantique and Transall was the Rolls-Royce Tyne, built under license by companies from France, West Germany and Belgium, Italian companies later joining the former programme.

The failure in this case to create a joint company for engine development and production 'greatly complicated', it has been said, the problems of management.[8] Development of Transall was equally shared between France and West Germany, West Germany taking the lead in production, but the Atlantique was a very unequal project, Breguet dominating even in development.

Henri Ziegler has said of the Atlantique that the first priority was the creation of a company with an appropriate legal and financial framework, and he has implied that it was because this, 'the first and most successful cooperative programme' was on budget, met its specifications and made a profit that the same kind of framework was later sought for the European airbus.[9] The formal creation cf Airbus Industrie to manage the latter project was perhaps partly intended to still doubts about the management capacity of the collaborating companies, though the central organisation has remained small.[10] Airbus Industrie is formally a 'groupement d'intérêt économique' (GIE), the industrial entity made possible by French legal provisions of 1967, and seen by some as an interim arrangement pending harmonisation of European company law, and by others as a means of preserving the national identity of companies. The GIE form allows collaboration to be restricted to a single project, members are financially responsible in proportion to their share in the undertaking, and other formulae determine voting rights and profit and loss apportionment. The greatest drawback of the GIE structure is undoubtedly its provision for unlimited liability, its greatest virtue the extreme flexibility it allows.

The major backers of the European airbus project are, for development, the French and West German Governments, and for sales, a consortium of French and West German banks, and the major industrial organisations involved are Aérospatiale (France) and the Deutsche Airbus consortium of MBB and VFW-Fokker, with Hawker-Siddeley, Fokker-VFW and CASA (Spain) having lesser stakes. The Franco-West German agreement had to be sufficiently flexible to allow for the private involvement of Hawker-Siddeley, the British Government having withdrawn, and Hawker's role becomes a more important one as the emphasis shifts from development and production to sales. The industrial companies are themselves responsible for a percentage of the development costs, and if development estimates are exceeded the consequences fall immediately on Airbus Industrie and the contracting partners. The GIE form also ensures that only operating capital is required, and allows the partners for tax purposes to include the project in their total trading results.[11] But according to *Interavia*, 'Perhaps of even greater significance is the fact that Airbus Industrie illustrates the feasibility of establishing an organisation acceptable to interested governments which makes commercial collaboration possible across national frontiers'.[12]

Turning to projects involving the British Government, the essential difference between the Concorde organisation and those created later for Jaguar and the MRCA was that in the case of Concorde no joint companies were established. Instead, the French and British companies were made separately responsible, through joint directors committees, for the airframe and engines respectively, to an official Management Board, and through this to the high-level Official Directing Committee. Under the joint directors committees are other specialist committees, indeed a 'plethora of committees', but it seems to have worked and of itself not greatly to have contributed to cost escalation. The Anglo-French Martel missile project, 'a truly joint collaboration with the partners having equal status and with a contract let by the two Governments',[13] also falls broadly into this category. In this case again the international organisation overlaps the national organisations with a committee system rather than integrating them, and the contractual relationships between the two Governments and the respective companies are somewhat different, Engins Matra having a little more freedom than their opposite number Hawker-Siddeley. Of the Anglo-French helicopter package too it has been said that there exists a 'well-balanced inter-relationship between firms and officials of both countries', the industrial agents Westland and Aérospatiale participating in all committees except the administrative subcommittee of the overall management committee, having close and continuing contact through working groups and ensuring that their general managements meet at least annually.[14] For the Jaguar project, joint companies were set up, SEPECAT for the airframe, registered in France, and Rolls-Royce–Turboméca for the engine, registered in Britain, and this tighter industrial arrangement was paralleled by a simplification of the official arrangements over those drawn up for Concorde, the French Government placing the contract for the entire airframe and the British Government that for the engine. With Jaguar, Martel and the helicopter package all in hand, France was officially described in 1967 as Britain's 'major partner' in this field, and a joint defence board was created to supervise development and production programmes, the joint management committees for each project being responsible to Ministers through this board.[15]

The arrangement for the MRCA has been felt to be a 'considerable advance on previous organisations'.[16] This is because, although there is a government-level structure, the three-country policy group, 'NAMMO' and its executive arm 'NAMMA', responsible to these are the joint companies Panavia, registered in West Germany and owned by BAC, MBB (West Germany), and Aeritalia (Italy), Turbo-Union, registered in the United Kingdom and owned by Rolls-Royce, MTU (West Germany) and Aeritalia, and before it was wound up, Avionica.[17] There is actually something of an 'educational exercise' about the MRCA programme, the international memorandum on which it is based specifying the requirement to establish a capacity as well as to build an aircraft,[18] and the arrangements have been thought by some, including senior British Ministers, to offer a uniquely suitable model for future collaboration.[19] Panavia is a flexible organisation, the shareholdings of BAC, MBB and Aeritalia changing from thirty, fifty-five and fifteen respectively during the project definition phase to forty-two and a half, forty-two and a half and fifteen respectively during development, and it is especially noteworthy that Panavia itself announced in 1970 that it felt competent to initiate private venture studies of further military aircraft. Panavia has also been specifically contrasted even with SEPECAT, in that it has its own management structure, whereas the latter is a shell company without its own staff. On the other hand, it has been stated[20] that non-West German shareholders in Panavia are 'probably some fifteen per cent worse off' in profits because of the German withholding tax on dividends paid to foreigners, and some problems and delays due to the organisation itself have also been reported.

Organisational questions are thus undoubtedly an important feature of collaborative aircraft projects. Other current European collaborative aircraft programmes, such as Dassault's Mercure, the Fokker-VFW F28 Fellowship, the VFW 614 and the Alpha Jet,

have not been mentioned here at all. Only the last of these is in fact
a true intergovernmental programme, Dassault leading and Dornier
collaborating in an equal work programme. The first three are
simply industrially arranged development and production consortia, with Dassault, Fokker and VFW leadership respectively, but
also with government money available in each case.

It is not difficult to understand however, even from the small
number of cases which have been discussed here, how

> Management-type activities associated with international
> collaborative agreements, work-sharing and programme defini-
> tion can at times require almost as much attention as technical
> matters from line departments, let alone the project manage-
> ment teams who are continually involved with such issues . . .
> it is important to ensure that formal management procedures
> are not allowed to become an end in themselves, or to take
> emphasis away from sound engineering.[21]

The legal dimension of all this can also be very taxing, covering,
as it must, both intercompany relationships and the quite different
relationships between contractors on the one hand and governments
and – or customers on the other. However, law can supply only the
bones of a project, and 'the legal form is irrelevant to the prime
requirement of an explicit and comprehensive collaboration agreement formalising the relationship of the parties'.[22] The author of
this quotation, W. B. Jenkins, has itemised the issues to be settled
as including attribution of liability, industrial property rights,
termination provisions, and the need to restrict collaborating parties
from joining with others in competing projects, bearing in mind the
difficulties of defining 'competing', and also the existence of anti-
monopoly laws. He adds that as well as the legal structure and a
more flexible management framework, 'it is invariably the case that
in international cooperative projects, the participants find it to be
necessary to superimpose . . . some basic ground rules within the
context of which major decisions . . . are to be taken'.

The last word on the organisational aspect of European collaboration in aircraft production can usefully be left with the editor of
Aviation Week. Giving the Royal Aeronautical Society's Barnwell
lecture in 1971 Mr Hotz argued that the formidable problems of
realising Europe's potential were 'primarily organisational and

fiscal rather than technical'.[23] He added that Europe had 'tried a number of organisational patterns to fit various bilateral and multi-national programmes', and felt that the fact that some of these patterns had worked must surely be 'astonishing to many observers and perhaps some of the participants'.

Questions of Organisation: Space and the Nuclear Sector

In the space field, where Europe chose to establish in ELDO and ESRO two quite different sorts of body, it would be fair to say that ELDO's organisational form helped to precipitate its undoing. Unfortunately, at the outset 'it was much less well appreciated than later that a really powerful centralised management was strictly necessary'. It followed that, whereas as the Director-General of ESRO, Professor Bondi felt that he had 'just about the necessary powers', he thought that as Secretary-General of ELDO 'one would not have had adequate powers for one's responsibilities'.[24] Because of the delay in the ratification of the ELDO convention, governments began to place contracts at their own risk, and this practice continued even after ELDO was legally in being. But government departments placing contracts on ELDO's behalf both made for a protracted process and put a barrier between the ELDO secretariat and the contractors, who understandably elected to address themselves whenever possible not to ELDO but to the departments. The predictable result was that 'the frightening complexity of this type of coordination had a direct influence on the choice of some technical solutions'. Paradoxically, ELDO's launch organisation was much better, but this naturally could not compensate for poor construction.[25]

By contrast, in ESRO the central organisation was large enough, and from the first had the standing, to control work satisfactorily itself, so that it was even necessary by 1967 to decentralize some of the decision making.[26] Two other organisational differences between ELDO and ESRO also deserve mention. First, ELDO was more a project-oriented body, whereas ESRO was charged with building up a capability, and this gave ESRO more flexibility. Second, the voting procedures drawn up for the two bodies were different. Such procedures are revealing because they exemplify the compromise struck to safeguard the interests of the member states without, so far as possible, simultaneously frustrating the international organisation. Both the ELDO and ESRO conventions contained provisions for simple majorities, for two-thirds majorities and for unanimity in specified instances, but the ELDO convention also provided for 'special two-thirds' majorities, which had to include countries providing at least eighty-five per cent of the organisation's funds.[27] Thus, while the annual budget in ESRO could be settled by a straight two-thirds majority, in ELDO the special two-thirds stipulation applied. This allowed the possibility of veto by a single country and in 1966 was amended, to countries providing two thirds of the funds, because of this.[28]

The ELDO crises of 1965 and 1966 at least led to the announce-ment that the secretariat would in future place new contracts directly. Reforms were also, it was stated, to be carried through in the internal management and advisory structures, and a corps of inspectors was to be formed.[29] In due course the SETIS organisa-tion was created with the help of the French SEREB company to act as consultant engineer, and the ELDO organisation then began on its second phase.[30] Unhappily, ELDO's technical discomfiture was not over. It was still unable to achieve a wholly successful launch of its composite vehicle and a new nadir was reached with the failure of the Europa II F11 flight in November 1971. The organisation was forced to set up a review commission into the circumstances of this failure and this commission not unexpectedly produced a report highly critical of the organisation and of its methods.

The commission found that despite the steps taken earlier to strengthen the organisation, the involvement of national agencies in contracting, political pressures and ELDO's own weaknesses, had all combined to deny the organisation the technical authority it should have had.[31] There were said to be shortcomings in both proving and manufacture of certain components, but the organisa-tional deficiencies were most clearly revealed by inadequacies in overall integration of the programme, and specifically in loose management of the electrical interfaces, almost automatically disastrous lapses where parts were being manufactured, not just by different companies, but by different states.[32] It is salutary to reflect that the subsequent development of European space policies might have been very substantially different had all stages of

ELDO's launch vehicle worked as well as the first, and worked together.

One could hardly wish for a better example than ELDO of the correlation between organisation and performance, but the organisational complexities of the European space effort do not end with the internal problems of ELDO. To begin with, both ELDO and ESRO were made responsible to Councils, and these have met at least twice a year, acting as legal and political authorities for the two space agencies. But mention must also be made, to demonstrate the general confusion, of CETS and the ESC. CETS, the European Conference on Communications Satellites, was set up in 1963 by nineteen European countries. It was given a permanent secretariat, in London, and one might have expected from its origins that it would function as the European equivalent of the powerful COMSAT company, which has acted as the American agent in the INTELSAT communications agreements. In fact, CETS's members never gave it the necessary authority, and later delays also helped to encourage the separate Franco-West German agreement for the Symphonie satellite programme.

To coordinate the work of ELDO, ESRO and CETS, the ESC, European Space Conference, was formed as a continuing body in December 1966, and in its first year it gave rise to the Causse Report which sought to bring order into European space policies, but in this neither the report nor later efforts by the ESC proved to be very successful. By the time this book appears however, a European Space Agency (ESA) may have begun to take shape.[33] The ESC agreed at its December 1972 meeting, largely as the result of a British initiative, to set up this body as soon as possible. It will, at least initially, be an agency of coordination rather than of collaboration, each country being free to join such programmes as it chooses, the ESA performing its main role in integrating national, bilateral and multilateral programmes. So confused has the total European space effort been that even this would be a valuable achievement.

In the nuclear energy sector European collaboration, as shown in the last chapter, is probably still gathering momentum. Even so, one lesson has already been learned, as can be seen by considering ENEA, FORATOM, the West German-Benelux fast breeder reactor and the Tripartite Enrichment Project. ENEA was established by the OEEC in 1958, its origins, like those of Euratom, lying in the fears of a growing energy gap in Western Europe. Its three main projects have been the Eurochemic fuel reprocessing plant, the Halden research reactor, and the DRAGON demonstration high temperature reactor. Most West European nations are members of the organisation and are allowed to choose the projects in which they wish to participate.

ENEA too had to adjust its role, but did so with more success than did Euratom. It has been said of ENEA that it

> has had a happier-than-most experience in the organisation of international collaboration on technical projects with commercial exploitation potential. Or perhaps it would be more correct to say that they recognised at an early stage the industrial and political conflicts involved and have maintained a powerful and tactful legal force.[34]

Of course, ENEA's objective has been much less ambitious than Euratom's, really only to provide a flexible organisation which would encourage international initiatives in the development of nuclear energy, but even this was not without political pitfalls. ENEA's Director-General stressed in 1968 that future policy would be to involve industry very closely from start to finish in new projects, a policy which had already begun to bring the organisation into a closer relationship with FORATOM, its opposite number, as it were, on the industrial side. FORATOM groups the national nuclear forums of each of the ENEA member countries, these forums themselves representing, not equally effectively, the voice of the nuclear industry in each country. FORATOM has played a valuable part in facilitating European industrial contacts, and since 1967 has moved more positively to promote a European approach. Working groups have since reported, for example, on the organisational and financial aspects of European collaboration in uranium enrichment, and on fuel reprocessing in Europe, and FORATOM-ENEA committees have studied the gas and steam fast breeder reactor concepts.[35]

No startling achievements can be attributed to ENEA and FORATOM, but their limited success, by contrast with Euratom's troubles, is not to be measured in terms of projects brought to fruition, but rather in terms of the general climate engendered. A suitable climate and the identification of true self and mutual interests which it enhances, would ideally be prerequisites of full commitment in all collaborative programmes.

It was shown earlier that in reactor development and exploitation it has come to be realised that the onus is best borne by private manufacturers, with perhaps an increasing role for the utilities. A very good example of this is the West German-Benelux fast breeder reactor programme. This has been described as 'truly international' in that: 'There are three levels of cooperation: the level of the base programme, the level of the industrial programme and the level of the utilities . . . early cooperation of industries is a necessity for international development'.[36] Only in the case of nuclear fuel cycle activities do governments retain a major role, because of the security angle, because of cost, because these are services whose long-term reliability must be guaranteed, and because of historical accident. Even here governments are increasingly aware of the need for a commercial approach to collaboration, the tripartite project, for example, is claimed to have been established such that its nature was from the outset 'basically industrial and commercial'. Two organisations were set up in this case, with opportunities for the association of private companies and capital, the prime contractor CENTEC to manufacture centrifuges, and the second organisation URENCO to use them, it being understood that both would have as much autonomy as possible, and that CENTEC would integrate and assume responsibility for the relevant R & D programmes previously being run by the three governments.[37]

Equity and Efficiency

After problems inherent in the administrative structure of collaboration, questions of equity and efficiency fall logically to be considered. It has with fair justification been said that 'The concept of fair shares and equality of treatment has become established as a, if not the, cardinal principle of European collaboration',[38] and it is to the problems inherent in this that one now turns. It is useful in this case to begin with Concorde.

The contracts and subcontracts for this programme were to be so distributed that the total cost was borne equally by the two countries, the major allocation of work being fixed at three to two in

France's favour on the airframe, and two to one in Britain's favour on the engine, with the work on the airframe expected to be approximately in the ratio of five to three with that on the engine. Following the initial division only one major work transfer had thereafter to be made to preserve the balance, but there continued well into the programme to be provision for adjustment, and the British also wanted a formal understanding that, in the event of a final imbalance in excess of two per cent, a financial adjustment would be made.[39]

Britain's Comptroller-General was told in 1965 that, while the aim was naturally to reconcile equality with economy, 'ultimately' equality was the 'predominant' consideration. As the Permanent Secretary in overall charge of the British side admitted, had the principal criterion been efficiency, then a fifty-fifty division had quite possibly been wrong to begin with. However, only if there developed a 'serious unbalance' or 'significant additional costs' was the problem to be referred back to the Governments. Characteristically, the House of Commons Public Accounts Committee were unhappy with this arrangement.[40] They were later informed that

> conducting this as an Anglo-French project makes it very much more rigid and prevents the Government having that degree of flexibility which it has in all its own contracts, because in addition to what it wants to do ... there is the question whether the French will wish to do the same thing at the same time and then what the contractual relationship is between the two governments.[41]

The Committee themselves stressed in 1966 that the likelihood of more collaborative projects made urgent 'a thorough study of the efficiency and economy of the sharing arrangement', but the official reply they received was that for the purpose of running other such projects, a formal review of Concorde experience would add nothing beyond what was already known.[42]

Another equity problem occasioned by the joint nature of the Concorde project concerned the intramural costs of the programme, costs that is, incurred by existing government research establishments.[43] When the project started Britain had already spent some £2 millions on extramural contracts, and a 'considerable amount' on intramural work, but the Ministry of Aviation did not feel that there was any justification for trying to include the latter in the joint agreement, since much of it was basic research. By February 1965 the estimated intramural cost to Britain was £7·3 millions, and it was then acknowledged that these costs had 'considerably exceeded' estimates in each of the previous three years. Two years later the Public Accounts Committee were alarmed to discover that the estimated intramural costs to Britain had now climbed to £28·4 millions. The Ministry, conceding that this was another point on which the Treaty was ambiguous, explained that they had nevertheless pressed the French hard to have these costs included, but the French had refused, claiming that they could not work out their own parallel costs. This was a situation in which there was no chance of switching the work from one country to the other because of the specialised staff and equipment involved, but also one which would presumably not have arisen had it been possible for the work to be done at the British contractors' plants rather than in government laboratories. Still other controversial questions as to what exactly was included in the Concorde agreement arose from the fact that certain earlier British aircraft and engines had also, in the eyes of some commentators, contributed to some extent to the Concorde R & D programme.[44]

It was possible to decide the division of work on Concorde virtually at the outset, and again on Jaguar to preserve a theoretical equality, but when the Anglo-French helicopter package was agreed one of the three helicopters (Puma) was already flying and the second (Gazelle) was well advanced in development, so that the division of work on the third had to provide for an overall balance. This resulted in a development sharing ratio of sixty-five per cent to Britain and thirty-five per cent to France on the third helicopter (Lynx), with Westland having design leadership, the only one of the six Anglo-French aviation projects for which Britain obtained this advantage. It followed that all equipment for the Lynx had to be selected against two parameters, a merit-cost ratio and the sixty-five to thirty-five requirement, and 'the second requirement often had to overrule the first'. This left Westland with a 'vast management responsibility', complicated further by the British and French devaluations, and by French requests for a revision of the sharing arrangements, following their cancellation of their army version of the Lynx and their decision to reduce their order for the Gazelle.

This cancellation actually lost the French the bulk of their original work allocation, and although as good as possible a reallocation was made, it was said to be impossible to restore full equality. All in all, it is not difficult to understand how even in this helicopter package, 'generally thought of as being among the smoothest-running of collaborative programmes', problems of equity proved burdensome.[45] .

In the Martel project, 'perhaps ideally suited for collaborative development, because in fact it is virtually two different projects with many common features', the problems of agreeing and coordinating intercompany interfaces, that is, matching workloads to funding provisions and industrial capabilities while still making engineering sense, were again discovered to be quite severe. Indeed, in this case, it was found to be necessary to maintain a team of people who would have been 'quite capable of performing the development themselves', but who were of course not allowed to, 'because of the collaborative nature of the project'.[46]

There are echoes here of a statement often made in connection with the MRCA, that this was an aircraft which Britain had the technical expertise, but not the funds, to build herself.[47] The division of work in the MRCA case was initially set at twenty-four per cent to Britain, fifty-six per cent to West Germany and twenty per cent to Italy, but this was adjusted to forty-two and a half, forty-two and a half and fifteen per cent respectively when West Germany reduced her order from six to four hundred planes.[48] Panavia from the beginning sought as policy, where possible, 'off the shelf' or 'minimum development' components, favouring in the selection process firms which had made transnational cooperative arrangements in order to bid, and the company also tried to circumvent the 'design leadership' problem by giving equal status to the British and West German chief systems engineers.[49] The first equity crisis in this project seemed briefly to concern the choice of engine, when it appeared that Britain might be going into the MRCA programme without a guarantee that Rolls-Royce engines would be used. 'There can be no question', *The Times* pronounced, 'of the contracts for the engines going outside the countries involved and the British Government would have done well to say so'.[50] In the event, the contract went to the second specially formed European consortium Turbo-Union, dominated by Rolls-Royce, and the major equity crisis centred instead on the avionics contracts.[51]

In this part of the project the third special consortium, Avionica, turned out to be an unworkable arrangement, and leadership began to be assumed by EASAMS, an Elliot Automation subsidiary. Several months were then lost as national commercial and political pressures compelled frequent reference back to governments, and the final choice of the radar system in particular was very badly received in Britain. In the Prime Minister's words, the British Government 'did its utmost' on behalf of the British avionics industry, but the key contract went to an American company on grounds of cost, and once more, as with the engines for the European airbus, it was said of a European collaborative project, that whoever did badly out of it, the Americans did well.[52] It is a matter of opinion whether the British companies could have lobbied still more effectively, perhaps in conjunction with West German interests. As it was, the possibility of contracts going to non-participating countries, apparently written into the Memorandum of Understanding, in this instance turned out to be highly damaging to the British avionics industry which, it was officially admitted, suffered thereby an important loss of experience.

In fact, of the many British industrial interests which have been affected for better or worse by collaborative projects, it is probably the avionics sector which has felt most ill-used. Avionics, and equipment generally, can now comprise some third of the cost of an advanced aircraft. Sharing the workload on such equipment can be just as politically sensitive and troublesome as on airframes or on engines, in that component selection normally depends on competitive tendering, often open, as with the MRCA, to non-participants, and such selection will not necessarily coincide with a politically predetermined work sharing formula.

It has been suggested that there is here an 'inherent conflict' to which 'far too little' serious attention has been paid.[53] The problem is undoubtedly made worse for Britain both because her equipment industry has been the foremost in Europe, and because she has so often exchanged airframe design leadership for aeroengine leadership, and avionics selection tends to depend rather more on the airframe authority. So it was that Elliot Flight Automation published a statement in 1970 which, while treating as unexceptionable the policy of British Governments in pressing hard for design leadership on engine development, yet decried the resulting tendency to make the airframe a second priority, 'leaving the design authority in the avionic and other equipment in the hands of the partners in the venture'. The statement added that Britain's partners were in consequence well-placed to use collaborative projects to develop their own avionics companies, typically with American assistance. The lesson drawn was a bitter one: 'The joint Anglo-European projects have not enlarged the British share of the avionics market and it is demonstrable that they never can do so.'[54] In the same vein, the Electronic Engineering Association has argued that, however strong the other arguments, collaboration must be justified by increased markets, but that for British avionics, because of the new capacity created in Europe by collaboration, the opposite, an erosion of the competitive edge, has occurred. The Association has specifically indicted Jaguar: 'Extreme pressure was placed upon industry to negotiate manufacturing agreements in France . . . The terms imposed on British Industry were such that an enormous amount of know-how and development experience was given to France without any corresponding benefit to the industry'.[55]

In the case of the MRCA there was again deep concern in the British avionics and equipment industries that tenders had had to be prepared without exact knowledge of the contract conditions, and under circumstances in which industrial property rights were not being safeguarded, so that it seemed possible for information and designs to be passed on informally to third parties, that is, to rival American firms having ties with continental companies, and for royalties to be otherwise lost.[56]

This issue has also been taken up by Sir George Edwards, chairman of BAC, who in a major lecture has argued both that 'collaborative projects should not be undertaken for reasons of political convenience', and that it is 'nonsense to allow a partner to head a project for political reasons if he is not technically competent to do so'.[57] As a last example, the Society of British Aerospace Companies has described 'surrender of expertise' as a principal disadvantage of collaborative projects. Collaboration, they say, 'is only worthwhile for the most complex and expensive systems and where large orders are thereby guaranteed'. They make the interesting suggestion that sharing projects on the basis that 'each nation handles one or more in its entirety' should be borne in mind. The Society also claim in this connection that British Governments have not involved British industry as fully in the negotiations on collaborative projects as prospective partners have done their industries.[58]

It needs to be stressed that it is not a fear of technology transfer as such that is being expressed here, but rather alarm at unequal and potentially damaging arrangements. Otherwise, to quote a Ferranti spokesman, the issue is a red herring and 'if you can keep in motion you need not be afraid'.[59] Up to a point criticisms and fears of this kind are inevitable, the sources quoted mostly have, quite properly, vested interests, and other partners will also suspect in some cases that they have had the worst of the deal. At this point questions of equity become questions of accountability, and one can only point to the fact that there exists no neutral agency charged or concerned to determine the truth of a case.

Meanwhile, from dissatisfaction over equity it is but a short step, and one easily taken, to deprecate the politicians and officials who acquiesce in the distributions made. This is an issue to which *Flight International*, for example, has regularly returned: 'In government-to-government negotiations the École Aéronautique Supérieure training of most French aviation civil servants easily unhorses the Whitehall and Westminster Warriors' and 'European collaboration remains a sensible policy, but not on the soft terms which Britain negotiates.'[60]

If these observations are valid, then the situation needs urgently to be rectified. If they are not valid, then it is still very disturbing that they should so firmly be thought so by important sectors of industry. The episode which springs to mind in this context is the AFVG. When this was under consideration it was assumed that, since France already enjoyed airframe design leadership on Concorde and on Jaguar, (and was to have it on two out of the three helicopters), she would not be allowed it also on this aircraft. When France withdrew from the project the residual imbalance was correspondingly all the more embarrassing for the British Government. This aircraft and the European airbus most clearly demonstrate Britain's, and France's, dilemma. It is best understood by introducing Joucla's formal distinction between equal and unequal intergovernmental collaboration.[61] Joucla is much in favour of the unequal form, because it can involve more than two governments, because it limits government independence, and because it places overall direction in the hands of one company. Of the AFVG he says that Dassault were strongly opposed to British design leadership, and of the airbus that between 1967 and 1969 the British Government became very uneasy about the growing competence of the French aircraft industry, and therefore decided to withdraw from this further project in which France was to have the lead. Hence the dilemma, that, as he says, excluding the helicopter package, it has never once been possible to get Britain and France together in the same unequal project.

More generally, it may be recalled that the Downey Committee, reporting several years before the creation of Britain's Procurement Executive, felt that one of the most important things which Britain could learn from the French was the advantage of their 'more compact interdepartmental organisation and the greater authority and independence of their administration', these characteristics being facilitated by special training and staff continuity.[62] A British Minister has also conceded more recently that there is 'probably a closer relationship' between the French aerospace industry and Treasury than exists between their counterparts in Britain. 'I do wonder sometimes what the French use for money', Mr Corfield added, 'I am sure nemesis will come'.[63]

Advantages flowing from close understanding between officials and industrialists, and others from running a large national space programme, both cropped up in evidence to the Estimates Committee in 1966 as explanations of poor returns to Britain in the shape of contracts from ESRO. Belgium was said to enjoy the former and France the latter, and it was clear that both were achieving far more satisfactory returns than was Britain. This the Committee naturally found 'unfortunate', though they approved ESRO's emphasis on efficiency at the expense if necessary of equity, concluding that ELDO's opposite emphasis was politically convenient but technically unsound.[64]

This Committee heard that had the British Government not been the most convinced initial proponent of ELDO, then they might well have felt at the time that Britain's original financial share was, at 38·79 per cent, too high, particularly when Blue Streak had been 'presented to ELDO as a dowry on its formation', when Britain's allocation of the work, though probably fair in cost terms, seemed to contain a less-than-proportionate amount of advanced technology, and when the percentage contribution was indefinitely fixed. The actual percentage had apparently been a Cabinet-level decision.[65] It should, had it been calculated, like the percentages for the other members, on the basis of GNP, have been twenty-five, but it was Britain's willingness to carry 33·33, and then, when six of the smaller countries declined to join, 38·79, which is said to have proved 'decisive' in the creation of ELDO. The Treasury may nevertheless have been wrong in thinking that an adjustable scale of contributions would have been impossible to agree for ELDO, because in ESRO it was laid down that contributions were to be periodically revised with reference to GNP, Britain's contributions beginning at twenty-five per cent and dropping later to twenty-one. But even accepting the view of the Estimates Committee that Britain was not in 1966 getting value for money from ELDO, it is not difficult to sympathise either with the reply another of their strictures received. It was not, they were told, 'considered possible to determine as a general rule what the balance between national and international space activities should be'.[66]

When the Science Committee investigated Britain's involvement in ELDO and ESRO in 1971 they were informed that, although in ELDO a straightforward formula now applied to ensure an eighty per cent return, Britain's return had 'actually been a good deal more'. By this time too, the return from ESRO was also said to be 'reasonably satisfactory' and 'very close to the appropriate percentage'. Because of the earlier imbalances this 'appropriate percentage' had now been fixed by the ESRO Council at seventy per cent, weighting factors being used to allow for 'high' and 'low' technology contracts. The Committee were also told by industrial witnesses at this time that the Government had agreed to the Black Arrow *national* programme to give Britain a similar position to that of France in getting value from the *international* programme.[67]

All countries, then, from time to time and in all technological projects, are likely to be dissatisfied with their returns from collaboration. Equity problems can also manifest themselves in a form which has been called 'locational politics'. 'Locational politics' were much in evidence in the process of site selection for the new CERN accelerator in the late sixties, as indeed they were in the parallel instance of the new American machine. Crane's interpretation of the CERN case was that Europe's physicists, in spite of having 'the most highly developed international communication networks' began losing control over the critical decisions because European politicians had waned in their enthusiasm for European unity and for projects which demonstrated it.[68] The technically brilliant compromise scheme which led to Britain's rejoining the CERN project was therefore even more of a shrewd one, in that it not only overcame the problem of cost, but also, by requiring that the new machine be built adjacent to the existing site, dissolved the locational difficulties.

In general, as with all international organisations, the siting of those concerned with science or technology remains a potentially political problem, often for hard economic reasons, as well as on prestige grounds. Thus there were overtones of 'locational politics' before the decision to site the European Molecular Biology Organisation (EMBO) at Heidelberg, though it is of greater moment that EMBO during its lengthy gestation period had more serious problems of the general 'commitment' kind than did CERN.[69] A better example of 'locational politics' would perhaps be the choice of Munich as the European Patents Centre, because some sixty per cent of European patents are in English, compared with only twenty-five in German and fifteen in French.[70] Or, taking another contemporary example, Italy, which gave a home to the International Institute for the Management of Technology is also, it was announced in 1972, to have in Florence the long-discussed University of Europe. Another frequently cited example is ESRO, its facilities ESTEC-ESLAB, ESOC, ESRANGE and ESRIN being in the Netherlands, West Germany, Sweden and Italy respectively, and its headquarters, like that of ELDO, in Paris. It has in particular been suggested that the first of these facilities should logically have been sited in Britain or France, and that there was no real need at all for the basic research centre ESRIN.[71] Trickles apart, and excluding projects such as DRAGON, which, given its origins, virtually had to be sited in Britain, it is not infrequently argued that Britain has been insufficiently favoured in European collaborative programmes. But this is an issue even more notoriously open to bias than straight 'equity' questions; secondly, as was noted above in connection with the proposed European weather centre, Britain is now at least just as ready as any other country to play 'locational politics'; and finally, there are not in any case so many prizes to be won.

The problem of the 'fair return' is obviously going to be around for a very long time yet, and it does little good to pretend otherwise.[72] Its harmful effects can sometimes be minimised when a project is capable of division, without loss of efficiency, into more or less independent subsystems, provided of course that other considerations then allow these to be allocated internationally in proportion to contributions – the NATO Air Defence Ground Environment (NADGE) and Integrated Communications System (NICS) fit into this category, it has been suggested, though both have encountered other difficulties. A second approach is to spread the calculation over several projects and a number of years, though this runs into the problems of maintaining intergovernmental trust, as well as budget and industrial asymmetries. The third most favoured solution remains the encouragement of international consortia, with the objective of pushing the difficulties of allocation down from the political to the commercial level.[73]

The last word on 'equity politics' at large may be left with Mr Corfield,[74] then Britain's Aerospace Minister, in the context of know-how won at Woomera being passed on to the French Guyana site. In his words, 'This idea that you always have to get more out of it than you give away is really not on in the modern world. The other chaps are quite good negotiators too!' This at least puts the political process of European technological collaboration in its proper, diplomatic, context.

VI The Control of Collaboration

The Issue of Cost

The universally known characteristic of R & D programmes is their marked tendency to cost escalation. The risk and consequences of this unfortunately seem to be especially serious in collaborative programmes. Thus, writing of government contracts as 'the poison in the pie of plenty', Hill[1] concludes that one of the results of the 'growing tendency in Western Europe for governments as well as organisations to share . . . costs' is that 'accurate estimations of product cost, performance and processing time are beset with difficulties'. But apart from cost escalation there is in collaborative programmes an even more basic issue relating to costs, namely the effect on costs even at the outset of collaboration itself. And in the case of commercial items, the fact that a product has a higher unit cost as a result of collaboration may make it unsaleable to non-participating countries, and even prohibitively expensive to participating countries if in the meanwhile another alternative becomes available.

It seems to be extremely difficult to quantify the extra cost of collaboration even in the aircraft industry, where the subject has received most attention. In the case of Concorde, for instance, Ministers have consistently dismissed the possibility of determining the additional costs due to collaboration with anything like accuracy.[2] What in fact are the factors which affect such a calculation?[3] Among them, certainly, are differences in language, standards, methods and the effect of geographical separation. The technical status of the aircraft and previous experience of collaboration are other relevant considerations. The number of versions of the product and the number of production lines are obviously also bound to influence the outcome. More formally, the Ministry of Defence has identified four types of relevant factor: unavoidable departures in practice from the division of work initially agreed, the effect of relative price levels in the collaborating countries, the need to accept higher or lower technical standards in order to reach agreement, and coordination across the additional technical interfaces.[4] According to the Ministry, the fourth factor always puts up costs, by an amount depending on the project, ten to twenty per cent for an aircraft for instance, but the first three influences can operate in either direction.

In the face of so many variables one can only generalise, and two much quoted generalisations are those due to M. Henri Ziegler and Sir George Edwards, each having great experience of collaboration.[5] Their conclusions are quite compatible and the diagram drawn by Sir George is reproduced. It shows R & D costs up by a third, and manufacturing costs up by five per cent as a result of collaboration. These are eighty per cent learning curves, that is, the production cost component of both is based on an eighty per cent learning factor, and they are said to typify a reasonably sophisticated military aircraft. The main objectives of collaboration are clearly seen: to share the (increased) research, development and production costs by increasing demand, that is, by working as far over to the right of the diagram as possible.

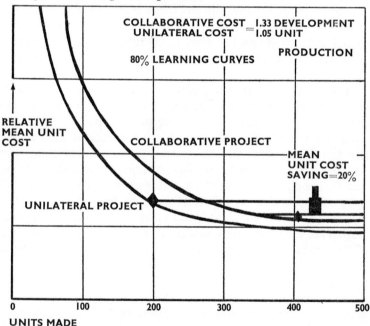

Cost Advantage of Collaboration. Reproduced from Edwards, Sir George, *Partnership in Major Technological Projects* (London: Oxford, 1970), p. 23.

The Concorde Programme

Against this background of more or less unavoidable cost increases in collaborative programmes one can proceed to examine briefly the theoretically more controllable cost escalation encountered in these programmes, though in view of what was said above about the difficulty of quantifying rigorously the extra costs due to the very fact of collaboration, doubts must persist as to what proportion of a final cost derives from normal escalation and what from the collaborative arrangement. The best example, though not a typical one, partly precisely because of the lessons drawn from it, is of course the Concorde programme. The main features seem worth retracing at some length here, if only because this aspect of the Concorde programme has received so much public attention as each new cost increase has been admitted that a balanced judgement has become correspondingly harder to strike. One would like to think that the facts had been thoroughly studied at the official level; they undoubtedly merit substantially more public analysis, as opposed to public sensation, than they have yet received.

The initial highly speculative estimate put before a British Cabinet committee in 1962 was £150–70 millions for a fully proven supersonic aircraft. The French thought the cost might be 'rather less', the British Treasury that it was 'idle to pretend . . . the estimates will necessarily stand up over a period of time'. Parliament in its first debate on the subject certainly did not expect them to.[6] The weakness at the outset was that the Anglo-French agreement had to be entered into before the time at which, had the project been wholly British, the Ministry responsible would have been prepared to award a development contract. With work only in the middle of the design study stage, the estimated cost at the beginning was 'not a great deal more than an inspired guess', and this for a project which turned out to be second only to the American space programme in technological complexity. By 1964 the cost estimate had risen to £275 millions, £65 millions of this being due to earlier underestimation, to inflation, and to programme alterations, while £48 millions were now provided to give the aircraft the requisite transatlantic range.[7] It was stated in early 1966 that there had again been an increase in costs, and by mid-1966 the official estimate had

Date	Estimates of total development costs	Estimates of UK share	Actual UK expenditure to date
November 1962	£150–70m.	£75–85m.	
July 1964	£280m.	£140m.	
June 1966	£500m. (including £50m. for contingencies)	£250m. (plus £30m. at R & D establishments)	
January 1969			£155m.
March 1969			£170m.
May 1969	£730m. (no provision for contingencies)	£340m.	
January 1970			£200m.
October 1970	£825m.	£405m.	£240m.
April 1971	£885m.	£440m.	£280m.
July 1971			£290m. (plus £10m. in production costs)
December 1971			£320m.
March 1972	£970m.	£480m.	£330m.

Successive Cost Estimates for Concorde

Reproduced from the 6th Report from the Expenditure Committee, Session 1971–72, *Public Money in the Private Sector*, HC347, p. 29.

risen to £500 millions, the increase once more being largely due to underestimation, wage increases and design changes, though at this stage £80 millions were also included for post certificate-of-air-worthiness development and £50 millions for contingencies. The latter was described as a 'sort of bulk allowance', over and above the contingency allowances which had been distributed among the various parts of the £275 millions estimate. The Government said at this time that they regarded 'the starting point of the failure to obtain effective control over commitment and expenditure' to be the open-ended nature of the initial Treaty, together with the fact that it had been entered into before the firms were 'effectively tied in'. There had by now begun to be widespread public criticism of cost escalation in the programme. The *Guardian* thought that the Ministry of Aviation's credulity was 'obviously and dangerously boundless', the *Financial Times* that the extent of cost underestimation was 'quite ridiculous'.[8]

Almost three years were then to pass before a revision of the 1966 estimate was released. The new estimate was for £730 millions. Of the £230 millions increase, £40 millions were said to be due to the British devaluation, £90 millions to pay and price increases, and that left £150 millions as the remaining real increase. Of this, £20 millions were put down to contractor overheads, £45 millions again to underestimation, and the rest to further design improvements. There was no longer an explicit contingency allowance, but with the scope for additional changes now said to be much less, there was in effect a hidden contingency provision, in that it was stated that not until the new estimate had increased by more than fifteen per cent – that is, by slightly more than £100 millions – would there be 'a demand for a fundamental redesign of the aircraft'. In this connection, the *Economist*, long a vigorous critic of the project, protested that a principal reason that costs had already quadrupled, was 'not because the estimates were wrong, but because the design was'.[9]

The next cost adjustment, in Britain's favour, followed the French devaluation of August 1969, when the cost in sterling of the outstanding French share of the programme fell by £25 millions. The next real cost change was announced in October 1970, the total cost then being put at £825 millions, £40 millions of the extra £95 millions deriving from pay and price increases, the rest from improvements. The official figures were revised again in the Spring of 1971, when the new cost was given as £885 millions, a quarter of the new increase yet again being due to pay and price increases, and half to more design improvements. By March 1972 the official estimate had climbed to £970 millions, with Britain then having spent £330 millions of a share estimated at £480 millions, but the Expenditure Committee said even of these figures that they expected them to fall 'substantially short' of the final total.[10] It had then been officially acknowledged for several years that considerably less than a third of this expenditure was likely to be recovered by a levy on sales, and that, as a Treasury official put it in 1971, there would therefore be a 'thumping loss' on Concorde.[11]

Some of the cost control problems which arose in the Concorde project derived from the contractual aspects of the government-industry interface.[12] British officials were unhappy with the original contracts, in particular because they did not provide for a specific contribution by the contractors to development costs, and great efforts were made in 1965-6 to introduce some form of incentive contract. British officials by then felt that the French, whose cost-plus-profit contracts were of a rather different kind, had definitely reached a point 'at which they are not a risk to us in this respect'. The two Governments finally agreed in September 1965 to waive contractor contributions to development costs, but it had still not been possible to include any incentive elements in the contracts by the autumn of the following year. All four main contractors were therefore 'summoned together and strongly addressed' on the matter by the Concorde Directing Committee. The observation of the Public Accounts Committee was that 'should this reluctance continue, it must be fully reflected in the profit rates that are negotiated with the firms'. Eventually, 'after difficult and protracted negotiations', limited incentive arrangements were agreed, but when these arrangements were in turn examined by the Public Accounts Committee, the Committee concluded that: 'Where, as in the case of Concorde there is a guaranteed minimum profit the incentive to reduce costs diminishes as costs approach the level at which the minimum profit operates and disappears completely when that level is reached.'

Further interface problems in the Concorde programme appeared in April 1966, when BAC informed the British Government that they would not be able to finance production.[13] They wanted the Government again to provide the funds and for themselves to be covered against loss; the Ministry on the other hand were anxious to avoid a situation in which the firms, taking no share of the risk, became simply the production agents for the Government. As Beaton complained: 'To have so great a project in the hands of firms which have no risk capital at stake inevitably puts the commercial judgements into the government's hands.' This riskless involvement having always obtained with respect to the R & D finance, the firms had really little to lose by refusing to accept a change. BAC for their part acknowledged in 1971 that the problem was one for which the right solution probably had still to be found.

In the event, the production finance arrangements announced in 1968 empowered the Government to advance BAC and Rolls-Royce up to £100 millions as an interest-bearing loan, and to rent to them £30 millions worth of special tools, and even the further £25 millions which was to come from the companies' banks was to be covered by a government guarantee. The total production finance available to BAC was further increased, to a maximum now of £350 millions, by a Bill of 1972.

Both the Labour Government and their Conservative successors were anxious not to commit more production finance than was absolutely necessary at any given time, but it was admitted in 1969 that expenditure for this purpose could not always be completely separated from R & D finance. The Expenditure Committee were told in 1971 that there was 'no intention that there should be a subsidy of any kind' with respect to production, but this Committee found it hard to deduce from published figures what exactly the Government anticipated having to spend on production, and, settling for a derived figure of £175 millions between 1971 and 1976, strongly recommended separation of the development and production figures.[14]

Apart from the main contracts, difficulties also arose during the course of the Concorde project in regard to subcontracts placed by the main contractors with firms in the other country.[15] This was because of the arrangement whereby such contracts were to be paid for by the subcontractor's Government, to avoid payment across the exchanges. There was an informal provision for officials to assist 'if requested' in the placing of subcontracts in their own country, but the British side thought that for them to have sought a more formal right to vet would have been unacceptable to the French, and bad business practice to boot. However, in early 1967 there was an imbalance on the subcontracts of some £6 millions, Sud having placed some £8·2 millions worth in Britain but BAC only some £2·2 millions worth in France. There had been some cost escalation, and it was known that the French would have liked from British subcontractors the actual costs of completed contracts, but of course this kind of equality of information was exactly what the British Government had for some time been seeking from contractors as a general rule of practice. As it was, the Public Accounts Committee simply condemned the fact that the Ministry of Technology had to pay a £6 millions excess 'over which they had no right to financial or technical control'.

Overall, government monitoring of Concorde costs seems to have been complicated, and indeed often frustrated, at least as much because it was such a complex and advanced project as because it was a joint one.[16] But it was left for each country 'solely to devise and be responsible for' the control of work done within it, each having a common interest in keeping down costs, and the British, though they felt at the beginning that French control might be less close than their own, were not worried on this count, because of this mutual minimum cost objective. Similarly, it was said on another occasion, with respect to cost control on the engine, that 'it would bedevil the scheme' if attempts were made to persuade the French to change to the British method.[17]

To check the adequacy of cost control in general a high level, joint team visited the four main contractors and nine subcontractors in late 1965, in an exercise which was said to be unprecedented on the international scale. The conclusion of this body was that 'in most firms the methods adopted for Concorde appear to have been an advance upon previous methods'. It was because of this that by early 1966 British officials felt they were getting to the stage at which the Concorde project would resemble for control purposes a normal (military) aircraft programme, and the Treasury were also by this time said to be 'reasonably satisfied' with the accountability of the project.

Later in 1966 it became necessary to press BAC and Sud for work programmes, but in spite of this, in spite of BAC's quarterly reports being late and in spite of officials having to question the accuracy of and control over BAC's estimates, the Ministry nevertheless judged the system of cost control to be at this time 'far in advance of any system that has ever been devised for any project'.[18] The matter of cost control having become the subject of some plain speaking between the Ministry and the Comptroller-General's staff in late 1966, it was later stated that because the management of the project was 'a shared operation between the Department and the firms', there were 'legitimate grounds for debate between the firms and the Department about how much control the Department should try to exercise, in what detail and in what depth'.[19] Despite this, it was thought officially by 1969 that the system was 'not far off as good as anybody can make it'.[20]

Other Aviation Projects, ELDO and ESRO

Early experience with cost control in the Concorde project was one of the factors which led to the setting up of the Downey Steering Group on Development Cost Estimating. The Group reported in December 1966, and several projects were afterwards cited by Ministers as having benefited directly from their work. Their principal recommendation, designed to improve the 'stage-by-stage' procedure laid down in the earlier Gibb-Zuckerman Report, was for 'a longer and more thorough Project Definition phase to replace the project study'.[21] The Group drew conclusions about the significance of this recommendation for international collaborative projects in general, and for collaboration with the French in particular. Having pointed out that, in its emphasis on early proto-type flight, the French philosophy of aircraft development differed fundamentally from the British, and also that the French had shown some willingness to move in the British direction, the Group said that they suspected that 'any move towards a longer and deeper exploratory phase', such as they were recommending, 'must under-line rather than reconcile the existing difference of approach'. Of international projects in general the Group concluded that

> we may not wish, or we may not be able, to persuade our partners to undertake Project Definition as a first step and before any commitment is agreed on full development. In such cases, we may have to commit ourselves earlier on full develop-ment than we should normally aim to do on a purely national project. This involves an extra risk, which should be recognised at the time.

The Downey Committee also commented on the proliferation of committees, with, they thought, consequent loss of unified direc-tion, characteristic of joint projects, and they noted that a Memor-andum of Understanding between governments could be open to different interpretations on such points as profit formulae, contract conditions and budgetary procedures, though they did not expect their proposals to make any difference to questions of this kind.

Time and cost schedules can be met in collaborative aircraft projects. This was shown with the technically straightforward Atlantique, and will be achieved, it is claimed, with the European airbus. Jaguar, one of the projects officially cited as having benefited from the Downey Report, was in its late development stages in 1971, and was then described as being 'well up to expectation', with its costs 'very close to the original estimates'. On the other hand, rumours had persisted that different priorities and requirements on the part of Britain and France were leading to financial and administrative strains in this project, and R & D costs had certainly risen, from £65 millions (1965) to £115 millions (1971), and production costs had almost doubled. It has however been argued that these increases are compatible with the original estimates, if allowance is made for inflation, for the British and French devaluations, for a halving of the joint order and for cost overruns of the Adour engine,[22] but there is, it seems, still room for discussion in this case.

Cost control was from the outset viewed as a major challenge of the MRCA programme, hence Panavia's policy of seeking minimum development components. The discipline forced on Panavia by the governmental agency NAMMA has been described as in all senses 'very strict', but it has also been recognised in this programme that 'reporting is not the whole of control but an effective follow-up discipline in giving results'. In line with this, it was decided that the right cost control principle to apply was 'not to detach groups to be responsible for costs as such, but to commit every group or department within the project to cost control on each discipline'.[23] Cost control is also a major aspect of the comprehensive government-level appraisals built into the programme as critical management checkpoints. Thus, the initial feasibility study having ended satisfactorily on 1 May 1969, the project definition phase then began; Britain and West Germany signed a Memorandum of Understanding on 22 July 1970, Italy declaring her continuing membership of the project on 1 October 1970; the next announcement of satisfactory progress, following a review, was made on 9 September 1971; and a further checkpoint was reached on 1 November 1972. And cost considerations, having been a major influence in determining which countries would collaborate on the MRCA in the first place, thereafter helped to prompt both a downward revision of the provisional German order, and the German and Italian decisions not to hold out for a single seat version. Furthermore, the Commons Expenditure Committee were told after the July 1971 review of the MRCA programme that, although progress was satisfactory, to hold down costs it had been necessary both to reduce the number of alternative weapon configurations and the number of development aircraft, and to settle for a common radar and the omission of other less essential equipment.

A final important point to remember on the subject of cost escalation in aircraft projects is that the Rolls-Royce collapse of 1971, having itself been caused by cost escalation on the RB211 engine, for a time cast doubt on the likely future costs of all Rolls engines. One such case, for example, was the Rolls-Royce–Snecma M45H engine for the VFW-Fokker 614 collaborative aircraft project. The West German Government had agreed originally to find half the development costs of this engine, estimated at £20 millions, and when its costs rose they were asked to pay half also of the increase. This they eventually agreed to do, making available some £17·9 millions, with the British Government themselves then having to contribute some £13·6 millions.[24]

In ELDO, cost control was 'one of the worst features'. Cost escalation in Britain was much less than that which took place on the Continent, where experience was originally much more limited, but the Estimates Committee concluded in 1966 that the really serious British error had been 'the failure to secure adequate safeguards for the British taxpayer against a rapid rise in costs'.[25] To be fair, when ELDO was established the various countries were to a large extent exploring the possibilities of collaboration and, as a Treasury witness told the Committee, it was thought that the provision in the financial protocol for further consultation in the event of cost escalation 'would enable some sort of control to be kept over the development costs'. Unhappily, in the words of another Treasury witness in 1967, this was an international expenditure 'and, therefore, less controllable than most'.

It was really an unfamiliarity with international collaboration which led the United Kingdom, in signing the ELDO convention, to the position that 'the commitment which prima facie they thought they were undertaking was to supply 38·8 per cent of an estimated cost to completion of £70 millions'. When costs rose, all the Treasury could do was 'to try and press for the best controlling machinery and accounting machinery that we could get set up by the organisation', since under the convention no country could withdraw until either the convention had been in force for five years or those programmes in which it had agreed to participate were completed. ELDO could therefore with some truth be criticised as 'essentially a machine for cost escalation'. A painful lesson having been learned, it was finally decided that legal safeguards could be incorporated in the financial protocol to remove the open-ended nature of the commitment, while still preserving adequate confidence in the programme. A member state not wishing to contribute to any overspend was obliged under the revised arrangements negotiated in 1966 only to ensure the completion of work allocated to its own contractors. A new stress was also now placed on fixed price or incentive contracts, the inclusion of penalty clauses being rather a hollow device in such a complex programme, but the financial provisions were, even after this, far from completely watertight.

In the end, the programme ceiling fixed for ELDO in 1968 was some three times the figure envisaged in 1961. In ESRO too, both capital and operating costs rose, but here, to keep within the agreed eight-year financial total (£110 millions at 1962 prices) activities were reduced and the eventual programme was 'considerably smaller' than had been envisaged at the outset. When the decision was taken not to proceed with ESRO's Large Astronomical Satellite (LAS), because it threatened to be 'vastly more expensive' than had earlier been foreseen, little had actually been spent on it, whereas in ELDO cost escalation became apparent only when a substantial expenditure had already been incurred. Unfortunately, and ironically, LAS was also the only ESRO project scheduled to use an ELDO launcher.

In view of the so far very limited collaboration in the nuclear sector, and its complete absence in the case of computers, examples of cost escalation are naturally easiest to find in the aerospace sector. Equally naturally, the phenomenon is more intractable in the case of the more technologically advanced projects like Concorde than in that of more orthodox products like Atlantique. And on the evidence, like initial project selection, it *is* more troublesome in collaborative projects. It has more than once been said of the aerospace sector, and the conclusion is probably as relevant for all technological fields, that more sophisticated formulae are needed than yet exist to cope with the stark alternatives of an open-ended commitment or the responsibility for cancellation. Meanwhile, there is real force in Brown's warning that 'unless the quest for interdependence is constantly informed by a strong sense of what is likely to prove effective in terms of cost it is bound to end in disillusionment'.[26]

Withdrawal Provisions

It follows too that there must be provision for cancellation, unilateral if necessary, in collaborative projects, awkward though it may be to negotiate mutually satisfactory and unequivocal terms at the very time when the commitment to collaborate is itself being negotiated. In this respect at least, the lesson of Concorde is not likely to be neglected.

The absence of a cancellation clause in that case is another well known cliché of the affair, but there really ought not to have been any surprise that the Labour Government felt it impossible to act independently when they took office in 1964. The Estimates Committee had questioned in 1963 the 'wisdom of entering into such a commitment ... in which no provision whatever was made for the possibility of the project being abandoned by one or other of the signatories'.[27] The Committee had received confidential information to the effect that for Britain to have suggested such a 'break clause' would have been to have offended the French, to which the Committee's reply was that, on the contrary, it would have been 'entirely natural and proper', since Parliament was being committed to a very heavy financial burden over the next decade. On their part the Treasury refused at this time to take responsibility for the fact that there was no break clause; it would, they said, be a matter for discussion between the two sides if ever withdrawal were to be sought by one of them.

It is now a matter of record that in October 1964 the new Labour Government announced that they were to carry out 'a strict review of all government expenditure ... cutting out expenditure on ... "prestige projects" ... The Government have already communicated to the French Government their wish to re-examine urgently the Concorde project'. The Minister of

Aviation defended this decision on the grounds that there was a great possibility that the already high costs would spiral further, so that 'by 1971 we might easily find ourselves in a position in which, without any hope of return, we had spent many hundreds of million'. With projects like Concorde, he insisted, it was essential that if there were any doubts at all about their economic viability, then there had to be worthwhile counterbalancing technological or social factors. In the specific case of Concorde the need for review was urgent, in that only some £7·5 millions having until then been spent by the British contractors, the point had been reached when actual costs would begin to rise steeply. He saw no reason why the long-term interests of Anglo-French collaboration or European unity should be damaged by a review of a project about which the Government had 'legitimate doubts'.[28]

The French response was a cold one. The French Prime Minister, M. Pompidou, complained that 'The position of the British Government consists in practice of delaying and in fact of abandoning the Concorde project . . . we can only regret [this] attitude'.[29] In January 1965 the British Government announced that they would stand by the Treaty commitment of their predecessors, though they retained their doubts about the financial and economic aspects of a programme which the Minister of Aviation still chose to describe as 'hazardous'.[30] It was generally understood that the French Government might well have brought the issue to the International Court if Britain had withdrawn unilaterally, and it was believed by some that the French did have a case in international law. The document setting out the formal agreement between the two countries was really an astonishingly brief one in view of the significance and cost of the project, and there was probably nothing in it which could definitely have ensured a successful French suit,[31] but even the threat of an international legal action was assumed to have been a formidable pressure on the British Government.[32] Not until later did it emerge that the French Treasury at least might have welcomed a firmer stand by Britain.[33]

The lack of any termination provisions in the Concorde project was in marked contrast to the clarity on this point even of the ELDO agreement, the most comparable commitment of the early sixties, and the Anglo-French package of the mid-sixties showed that it was perfectly possible to write into collaboration agreements clauses which permitted partners to withdraw, at least up to certain well defined points in a development programme. Thus the Anglo-French Memorandum of Understanding of 1965 covering Jaguar and the AFVG aircraft left each side with the opportunity of withdrawal on twelve months' notice, and in the case of the AFVG without notice at all until 1 June 1967, provided certain engine work, 'within agreed financial limits', was completed. In the AFVG case, the British Government actually agreed to extend the time limit to the end of 1968. An escape formula was similarly written into the MRCA agreement reached between Britain and West Germany in July 1970. It was then stated that although the understanding covered a three-and-a-half year period,

> A thorough review of progress will be made at the end of one year in the light of the more refined assessments of cost, timescale and performance which will then be available . . . If the programme is not running according to plan there are arrangements for the partners to agree together about steps to be taken to rectify the situation, and it would be open to a partner to withdraw completely.[34]

The comprehensive review of the MRCA programme in November 1972 was, like that of July 1971, intended as a possible window for unilateral termination. This was allowed without compensation if the preliminary results of the programme were by then shown to be unsatisfactory, otherwise compensation to the end of the phase had to be paid to the remaining partner or partners. Future civil projects will presumably be treated like those in the defence sector, where the Ministry of Defence has said that it is now 'normal practice' to allow unilateral withdrawal, subject to a substantial and prearranged period of notice, and with the 'obligation to pay the appropriate share of costs in the meantime'. The Ministry has also commented on this whole question that

> although Memoranda of Understanding do not have the status of formal International Agreements the provisions relating to the duration of a programme nevertheless represent solemn undertakings which it would be a very serious breach of good faith for any country to break.[35]

The characteristic effect of collaboration on depth of commitment and on opportunity for withdrawal was forcibly expressed from the industrial viewpoint by Sir George Edwards, Chairman of BAC, in 1972.[36] Sir George finds a fundamental problem in his industry's dependence on a sound working relationship with government, the essence of the difficulty being, he feels, that high technology is long-term, whereas matters of politics are short term. In his words,

> Long-term stability is essential if the nation is to obtain value for money from advanced technology . . . these international programmes in Europe try men's very souls, but . . . collaboration puts an iron rod through what would otherwise be a jelly programme . . . they are very difficult to get started but they are also almost impossible to stop.

As Sir George adds, there is in consequence an exceptionally high premium on getting thoroughly sound decisions, and getting them absolutely at the outset.

Following this, it needs to be recognised that newly elected governments, or even newly appointed ministers, whether or not of the same political party, will often want as soon as possible to review expensive ongoing projects, yet only fortuitously will such times coincide with natural checkpoints in development programmes. There could scarcely be a clearer demonstration than this of the way in which the requirements of efficient, technocratic, administration can differ from those of democratic politics. This is a problem which can, and does, manifest itself in wholly national programmes, but it is naturally more likely to occur in collaborative programmes, and more likely to occur the more governments there are involved.

The Parliamentary Dimension

It is well understood that governments face special problems in monitoring and controlling the complex technological projects which in whole or in part they decide to fund, and it is also generally recognised that these problems are paralleled by others which confront parliaments and their agents in trying to ensure that such projects are as fully 'accountable' as any other of the activities of government. What is less clear is the extent to which these problems of accountability are affected by the fact that a project is being undertaken collaboratively. As things currently stand, one cannot really look to the quasi-parliamentary bodies at the European level to meet the need, though each does its best with the very limited powers at its disposal, the European Parliament with respect to Community programmes, the Science and Technology and other committees of the Council of Europe, and the Committee on Scientific, Technological and Aerospace Questions of the Western European Union, with respect to wider European activities. These bodies are naturally concerned primarily with the European dimension of policy, or the lack of it,[37] but it is also interesting to note how, in their treatment of the supersonic aircraft for example, other parliamentary committees at the European level have sought to realise a wider accountability.[38] For their overall inadequacy these European bodies are not to be criticised. They were never intended by the governments which allowed their creation to be serious instruments of accountability.

The British Parliament's difficulties in securing accountability in a technological project, and the uncertain effect on these difficulties of the collaborative dimension, have both been well illustrated by the treatment of the Concorde case at the hands of House of Commons Committees. Concorde has been investigated by the Estimates Committee, frequently, though with one unhappily long gap, by the Public Accounts Committee, and at the time of writing, most recently by the Expenditure Committee. The substantive content of these various investigations has been referred to elsewhere in this book, and the emphasis here is on the idea of accountability more generally.

The early report on Concorde by the Estimates Committee was a valuable one which highlighted several shortcomings of the project, notably the lack of a cancellation clause, and the several reports by the Public Accounts Committee have been well up to that Committee's usual high standards, but here there have been difficulties.

First, the Committee in their 1969 review were much exercised that three years had gone by without a public revision of the cost estimate for this project, so that when it did come it was massive. They objected that:

Where so much public money was at stake Parliament should

have been made aware at more frequent intervals of the escalating estimates and of the slippage in the programme, so that informed debate could take place on the justification for continuing with the project.[39]

The Treasury's reply on this point was that it had been 'judged inadvisable' to announce changes in the estimates while negotiations on incentive contracts were in progress, or before agreement with the French Government, but the Minister of Technology acknowledged in the same year that there was indeed 'too little information generally available about the Concorde project'.[40] One can only assume that Ministers were persuaded by the arguments put forward by their officials, because a Government which was known to have tried and failed to cancel the project ought not to have found too embarrassing regular confessions of cost increases. Yet the Treasury's argument can hardly have been fully convincing. Contingency allowances were included in published cost estimates, and even though firms were denied knowledge of the separate contingency provisions made for each of them, they did know what their own real cost increases had been, and they knew also that the Ministry would perforce have to base revisions of the contingency allowances on these figures. The Government certainly seems to have been somewhat remiss, but where also, one might ask, were the Comptroller-General's department and the Public Accounts Committee in the interval?

The Public Accounts Committee have evidently experienced special difficulties in handling Concorde. Their chairman acknowledged regretfully in 1966 that: 'One of the by-products . . . of this international cooperation is that we have felt bound not to publish rather more of the evidence than we would had this been a wholly British project.'[41] There had on this occasion been a division within the Committee as to whether a cost figure of £500 millions should be published, the Comptroller-General having asked for it to be sidelined. The Financial Secretary to the Treasury, stating later that he thought the Committee had been right to publish, at the same time thanked them for timing their report so as to allow the matter to be settled with the French. Part of the Committee's problem with Concorde was expressed by another of their members in 1969:

Traditionally, the Public Accounts Committee has examined the men directly responsible for spending public money – accounting officers. But the senior civil servants do not really spend money on projects like Concorde. They try to exercise control and surveillance over the firms spending money ... This kind of spending on advanced technological hardware seems to throw up new problems of control and examination.[42]

Hence also one can sympathise with the observation of the Committee's Chairman in 1969, that it would be a 'happy day for the Committee when the Concorde comes off its menu'.[43]

In 1971–2 the objectives and control of the Concorde project were examined by the new Expenditure Committee.[44] This Committee wanted in particular to know the engine cost estimates separately from those for the airframe, and to have details of the price formula which had been settled for the aircraft. These figures the Department of Trade and Industry declined to give. On the first point, the argument which had been used earlier was repeated, namely that published estimates were higher than the sum of the estimates obtained from the several manufacturers, and to publish a detailed breakdown would be to tell the latter what contingencies were provided in each of their cases, thereby weakening discipline and strengthening the manufacturers' hands in financial negotiations. To both of the Committee's inquiries the Department replied that, while the Committee's interest was 'fully appreciated ... very substantial sums of public funds would be at risk if the information requested ... were disclosed'.

The Committee were also told that 'the French are partners and we cannot move without their consent', and that had information of the sort they wanted been published earlier, then the cost situation 'could be even worse'. Sir Robert Marshall carefully explained the authority of the Department's reply to the Committee:

We are denying to Parliament information which you have asked for. In doing this, obviously a reading has been taken of the public interest ... we obviously felt it necessary on a matter such as this ... to seek the guidance and instruction of our Ministers.

The Committee noted that Sir Robert was unable to quote a

precedent in the civil sector, that he had added that the information would probably be withheld for a long time, and that they understood Sir Samuel Goldman to have said, in the Committee's words, that 'such a policy would involve adjustments in the annual White Paper on Public Expenditure to hide the extent of the recovery of development costs'.

Refusing to, as they put it, abdicate their duty to scrutinise Concorde expenditure simply on the grounds that by their scrutiny they could be charged with 'knocking' the project, the Committee returned again and again to their main theme of more openness in the public interest, justifying this demand by the facts that Concorde was a monopoly product and that there was no element of true profit involved, and by their opinion that public pressure flowing from public awareness of the full facts would strengthen officials in negotiations with manufacturers and customers. The Committee asked for an annual Concorde White Paper and for more frequent *ad hoc* information, concluding that: 'It is our view that there has been inadequate Parliamentary control and too little information publicly given . . . continuous and informed Parliamentary and public comment is essential to the proper control of future large scale projects of this kind.'[45]

By contrast with Concorde, the various Anglo-French defence projects have received relatively little scrutiny from House of Commons Committees,[46] but there have been signs that oversight of the MRCA will follow the former rather than the latter example. Only the Expenditure Committee has so far been active with respect to this project, but having in 1972 discovered the great size of the programme, and having learned that costs had already tended slightly to escalate, and that the immediate future would see vital decisions made, the Committee determined that they would re-examine the project at an early date, so that the results of the major monitoring effort being mounted by the Ministry of Defence would be available to Parliament. The evidence taken by the Committee in their first inquiry was heavily sidelined and to this the Committee objected bitterly;[47] their complaint would perhaps have carried still greater weight had they discovered how much of the information removed was available from other sources, and put it back in.

That successive Governments have been unnecessarily secretive about aerospace matters is a hardy British perennial. To instance this it is convenient to quote again here, as a respected authority in its field, the journal *Flight International*.[48] According to this journal 'Apart from being a management cost-control tool, the public filing of costs is technology's duty to democracy'. In the spirit of this quotation, learning of complaints in the French National Assembly about cost increases in the Jaguar programme, complaints *Flight* believed it could show were mostly erroneous, the journal commented that: 'Being traduced is the penalty of refusing to give Parliament, Press and public the information to which they are entitled.' Similarly, of the sidelining in the MRCA evidence to the Expenditure Committee, the journal, with a particularly pungent turn of phrase, complained that 'The asterisks . . . imperil not only aerospace but democracy'.

Of Concorde, when in May 1972 the Aerospace Minister announced an £85 millions increase, the journal asked him if he would publish a breakdown of the £40 millions of this which were said to be due to additional development and revision of estimates rather than to inflation. The reply received was in such general terms as to add virtually nothing to what was already known. The journal, accepting fully that not all the information surrounding the Concorde project could be published, then suggested that since the Minister had to make decisions on highly technical matters, he needed as much assistance from all sources as he could get. It recognised the depth of ability in the technical civil service but believed publication to be in the interests of the aviation industry because of the industry's need for the continued support of society, and it added that: 'The knowledge that cost targets are open for all to see is perhaps the greatest single incentive to better cost-estimating and performance – by civil servants as well as by those who actually do the work.'

The observations of Parliamentary Committees and of a noted aerospace journal have been cited here at length, not by any means because these are the only sources of this kind of criticism, but because they happen to be particularly good examples from the political-administrative and technical points of view respectively. In Britain the topic remains as common as the weather, and the matter at issue perhaps as little open to change.[49]

Aircraft apart, other Anglo-European collaborative projects have from time to time been examined by Parliamentary Committees, the

Committees mostly following their usual methods. Thus, European space collaboration was quite fully, though perhaps not too objectively, considered by the Estimates Committee in two reports of 1966–7, and then by the Science Committee in 1970–71, and the much smaller collaborative aspect of the computer industry was touched on, also by the Science Committee, in sessions 1969–70 and 1970–71. Anglo-European nuclear collaboration has been less well served, for good reasons. The Estimates Committee welcomed the collaborative aspect of the DRAGON project in 1959, though they were slightly worried that the AEA might not otherwise have thought the system worthy of development at that time; and in 1967 the Science Committee were all for Britain proceeding alone with the DRAGON type of reactor if ENEA elected not to continue with the project.[50] In general, however, these Committees, and the other Parliamentary Committees which have concerned themselves with nuclear energy, have all found it necessary to concentrate on problems of much more immediate domestic significance than DRAGON.

A point of central importance in all collaborative projects is naturally the contractual element, and for this reason it is worth noting finally what the authors of two recent studies on government contracting in Britain have had to say about the role of Parliamentary Committees in this respect. Turpin and Edmonds[51] have concluded respectively first, that a broader investigation of the contemporary principles and practices of contracting is more desirable than the detailed scrutinies conducted by the Public Accounts Committee and second, that Parliamentary Select Committees in general may lack the time, expertise and capacity to ensure a proper accountability in this activity. Are these conclusions strengthened by the phenomenon of collaboration? Some Parliamentarians certainly think so, as the following three examples show:[52]

Large parts of advanced technology are already the subject of international collaboration in Europe, and this inevitably removes them to some extent from national parliamentary control.

I am quite sure that the mere incantation of the terms 'technology' or 'Europe' does not absolve the House or the Public Accounts Committee from a most rigorous and detailed analysis of the control and use of public money.

It may well be that we shall now, as we approach membership of the European Community, find ourselves having to recast very profoundly the whole relationship between the audit department, not only of this country but of other countries with whom we shall be in joint cooperation, and the Parliamentary institutions of those countries within the Common Market.

VII   The Evaluation of Collaboration

The Problem of Criteria

It is virtually impossible to evaluate any of the European scientific or technological projects completely objectively, partly because most of them are ongoing projects, but even more because there are no 'reliable objective criteria of satisfactory performance, or of participant satisfaction'. This is a conclusion reached by the group which has probably given most thought to the question, the Sussex Science Policy Research Unit (SPRU). Professor Freeman, the Unit's Director, rejects both 'reputational' measures, based on surveys of the relevant reference groups, and 'commitment' measures, based on increases or decreases in funding, the former because of bias and lack of means for cross-comparison, and the latter because of the existence of extraneous political and technical factors.[1] He settles instead, very tentatively, for a mixture of these two measures together with the evidence of political and financial crises and the production of 'satisfactory hardware'. He is alive to the significance of sheer 'bad luck', but feels that in the past the source of difficulties has lain really 'in the form of intergovernmental arrangements, in the choice of objectives, and in the method of control . . . False expectations arose from misconceived goals, and a misconceived strategy'. Governments should not, in his opinion, join in collaborative efforts where a rival national project exists, where provision for cost and time overruns and for commercial exploitation are inadequate or if they are not as governments prepared 'to accept the abrogation of national sovereignty . . . in favour of a genuinely international mode of management'.

Pavitt's very thorough analysis of Europe's technological prospects leads him to the similar prognosis that 'until there is a real willingness to accept a greater degree of mutual dependence amongst European countries, Europe-wide programmes . . . are bound to fail'.[2] He too emphasises that collaboration involves each country in surrendering 'a sizeable lump of national sovereignty', and the associated problems he therefore judges to be more ones of diplomacy than of planning or management – 'Metternich would have been more at home dealing with many of them than Mac-namara'. He is afraid lest only the least promising ideas become European intergovernmental projects, and also that European-level bodies may find themselves at too low a level to take the key political decisions and too high a level to handle the managerial questions. In his experience, unlike tariff or agricultural questions, 'policy problems related to science and technology lend themselves very badly to incorporation in rigid, international treaties or agreements'. It follows that on his interpretation, in the science, technology and industry field the EEC Commission has been excessively pre-occupied with the pursuit of an executive power which itself really presupposes a political unity. The Commission's 'important, indeed irreplaceable' role should instead, Pavitt feels, be as conscience, analyst and catalyst of European action.

The Sussex study was undertaken on behalf of the Council of Europe as a special project, ironically, it seems, not without difficulties, themselves typical of European technological collab-oration.[3] It appears even more desirable that retrospective analyses of collaboration should be attempted officially at the national level, but it is unlikely that this has as yet been done systematically, at least in Britain.[4] One tends therefore to be forced back to the platitudes that, at one extreme, Euratom and ELDO have largely been failures, that at the other, CERN has been an outstanding success, and that Concorde, the most controversial, is also the perfect example of technical success and commercial failure. The European airbus too, for all that has been said about its being a technical and managerial success, has still to prove itself commer-cially. But at least in the case of this aircraft a reasonably balanced final assessment should in the end be possible. With Concorde on the other hand, because of the nature of technical spin-off, and of follow-on technology, not to mention the deep and conflicting emotions stirred by the project, a consensus of judgement may never emerge.[5] But if the aircraft does go into production one can at least expect more reliable information on both the above-mentioned technical counts, and as regards the questions of airport noise, sonic boom, upper atmosphere pollution and operating economics. Even then, the rightness of the balance struck between sales and subsidies will have to be judged against a background of costly, but unquantifiable, political and commercial opposition to the aircraft.[6]

For present purposes, DRAGON perhaps offers the clearest example of technical success clouded by commercial uncertainty. It has certainly been a technical success, and for this there are said to have been several reasons.[7] First, it is noteworthy that, on a reasonable interpretation, DRAGON stayed very close to its budget, R & D being cut back when this was necessary. 'Reasonable interpretation' because, second, the project was conducted in stages, a new agreement being reached to cover each stage, so that it could be held by determined critics that costs incurred during later stages really belonged earlier. Third, the project's objectives 'were at every stage clearly defined and not only were they considered from the start to be entirely feasible, but also to hold considerable promise'. Fourth, the project, which was given no legal personality, had 'the further advantage of the management having been in the hands of a single country' with a Board 'so constituted that technical matters were immediately within its grasp'. Fifth, the 'clear terms of reference and financing' made for 'minimal Government interference', and the project members were at all times 'primarily concerned with the success of the project as a whole, rather than its advantages to the particular signatory that they represented.' Sixth, the project having involved many firms, it has been claimed that links for the commercial exploitation of the reactor have been and will be the more easily arranged. It is only when one turns from these praiseworthy internal pluses that the problem of defining success really emerges. For the embarassing fact is that when DRAGON was undertaken there was no assurance at all that it would ever be an integral part of any commercial programme, and at the time of writing, more than twelve years and £40 millions later, there still is not. In this case, however, definite grounds for optimism have persisted, and the original act of faith could yet prove very fully justified.

It is instructive that Professor Bondi, formerly ESRO's Director-General, claimed for that organisation too a very important success in terms of the European commercial links which it had encouraged. He had regarded himself, he said, as 'a marriage broker between different European firms', and the 'chief lesson' to be drawn from ESRO was that it was possible to give leadership to industry 'in an international framework as well as in a national one'.[8] A 'consistent industrial policy' had led to the formation of several European consortia on the threshold of international competitiveness. By 1972 there were in fact some five such consortia – CESAR, MESH, EST, COSMOS, and STAR – as well as the CIFAS consortium formed for the Franco-West German Symphonie programme.

Since ESRO was during its early years concerned only with science, one might expect that it would also be possible to evaluate it on that score, but again, except in very general terms, this is impossible to do. However, an index with which the Science Research Council, ESRO's British client, has been much concerned is cost per experiment flown, a commendable business-like criterion.[9] No comparable criterion could be applied to ELDO, and worse, when ELDO was established, 'it was universally less well appreciated than it is now that without very clear purposes and aims and some measure of measurable benefits it would be very difficult to keep unity'.[10]

There is no occasion to dwell yet again on the difficulties faced by ELDO, except to note in the light of its experience that the general rule, that the more dubious the future of an organisation, the harder it becomes to recruit and hold high grade staff, takes on a particular force at the international level.

When so few definitive or even illuminating remarks by way of assessment can apparently be made about civil collaborative programmes in Europe, it would really be rather absurd to attempt here some kind of unhappy amalgam between retrospective and prospective cost-effectiveness analyses in the case of military ones. Some simple observations, it is true, can safely be made, such as, for instance, that it is presumably a clear indication of success and mutual satisfaction that Westland and Aérospatiale have considered extending their collaboration on helicopters. Otherwise one can only, rather weakly, press for full analyses, to be undertaken by those in a position to carry them through in the light of detailed internal knowledge. This is not a task for a parliamentary committee, but such a committee could with advantage elect to monitor its execution. It seems more useful, and it is certainly more encouraging, to continue an unsatisfactory discussion of evaluative criteria by focussing instead on CERN, as seen by Salomon, who offers a persuasive explanation for this, Europe's one really unequivocal success.

According to Salomon, the main contributory factors in CERN's successful development were: the political will which existed at the outset; the recognition of clearly defined objectives; financial and personnel requirements too great for individual governments to bear; a need at all stages for real teamwork; administration in the hands of scientists who were substantially independent of governments; and an 'intellectual output' which was more important than a *juste retour* on contracts. But, as he also says, CERN has no equivalent, and it is not easy to see how it could have one, at least in the technological and industrial sectors, as opposed to the scientific one. In his words,

> Europe is possibly the most suitable area in the world for scientific and technological cooperation . . . future development . . . depends upon the political 'mortgages' determining the future of Europe . . . The situation is paradoxical; there are pressing reasons for more extensive international cooperation but many obstacles.[11]

The Contribution to Integration

European technological collaboration, and cooperation, also need really to be evaluated in terms of their contribution, whether positive or negative, to European political integration. An assessment of this would obviously remain important even if political integration were held to be undesirable. As with all other evaluative criteria, the analysis ought to be on a case-by-case basis, but, unfortunately, again as with all criteria, the research which would allow this simply has not been done. There may indeed be no reliable scientific way of doing it, and for the present therefore, a more limited survey of the collaboration-integration relationship must suffice.

Invaluable as a point of departure is Taylor's interpretation of the usages currently attaching to the term 'integration'. Taylor points out that the term is almost invariably linked with value judgements, and that these are frequently not made explicit. He deals with both the narrower use of the term by theorists, and the broader use of it to describe real powers and policies arranged hierarchically, from *association* (e.g. the Universal Postal Union), through *harmonisation* (e.g. the Council of Europe) and *coordination* (e.g. the OECD), to *partial integration* (e.g. the ECSC), and eventually to the *integrated state* (e.g. the objective of European federalists). Taylor also shows that the theorists distinguish between integration as process and as condition, and he divides them into three schools, depending upon whether their primary focus concerns institutional and political factors (e.g. Etzioni), the dynamic forces of integration in a pluralist competitive society (e.g. Haas and the neo-functionalists), or the socio-psychological sense of consensus and community (e.g. Deutsch). Now, because the concept of integration has been introduced here only in the rather specific sense that it can be regarded as an evaluative measure, it follows that those theorists interested in the dynamic forces of integration are likely to have most to say about the potential, one way or the other, in this respect of technology. In the real world, of course, as Taylor so rightly says, 'The practitioner would indeed be well advised to invest in a portfolio of theories . . . [and to] strive for a state of mind which I would call one of strategic ambivalence'.[12]

If one begins from the position that technological collaboration is, in part, a form of economic integration, one can use Pinder's definition of the latter: 'the removal of discrimination as between the economic agents of the member countries, and the formation and application of coordinated and common policies on a sufficient scale to ensure that major economic and welfare objectives are fulfilled.'

Pinder calls these two approaches 'negative' and 'positive' integration respectively, the removal of tariff and non-tariff barriers being examples of the former, non-tariff barriers having special significance in the case of technology, while common industrial, technological and scientific policies would be varieties of the latter.[13] Quite apart, however, from being part of economic integration, as Pinder recognises, technological collaboration seems also to have special ramifications for political integration. This follows from the fact that it, and the industrial linkages to which it gives rise, often impinge on sensitive prestige questions and on national security, and around both of these areas complex psychological haloes form all too easily.

The ultimate significance of this dual political and economic nature of technological collaboration could well be very important.

By reference to the work of Hoffman, Belassa, Krause and others, Hansen has shown that the automaticity of the link between economic and political integration, as argued especially by Haas and Schmitter, is unsound, or at least inadequate. In particular, Hansen stresses the distinction which Hoffman and others draw between 'high' and 'low', or 'welfare', politics, the former centring on 'the vital interests of national diplomacy and strategy,' with regard to which 'nations prefer the certainty, or the self-controlled uncertainty, of national self-reliance'.[14] Now, without re-adopting the complete Haas-Schmitter economics-politics continuum, it does not seem implausible to suggest either that between 'high' and 'low' politics there may be some kind of middle ground, or that technological collaboration and cooperation may belong in such a category. Another way of putting this would be to maintain that joint scientific and technological activity could itself be arranged on a continuum running from 'high' to 'low' political sensitivity, a European nuclear weapons programme and CERN, for example, being respectively at either end. The interesting possibility is then opened up that the general momentum from economics to politics postulated by the Haas-Schmitter model, but denied by other theorists and indeed it seems by practical experience, could reappear here as a specific momentum. So that the relevant companies having, for example, built several airframes on a collaborative basis, the full integration of the European airframe industry might be held to be increasingly logical at successive stages. However, it still requires political decisions, not to mention commercial willingness, to convert logically indicated solutions into reality, and one comes back to three things above all: the *political* experience of past and existing technological collaboration; the relative national success in manoeuvring prior to each commitment; and the prevailing beliefs about the future, including extra-European challenges. But rather more fundamentally, if one accepts that collaboration is entered into to maximise returns, or, even more pessimistically, simply to ensure survival of a national capability, then momentum may gradually spring from the persistence of either of these motives, or from the dysfunctional consequence that collaboration may reduce future options in the direction of national independence. At the very least then, the growth of momentum seems a distinct possibility, and from this it would follow that one could regard technology as belonging in the middle ground between 'high' and 'low' politics.[15] In this context it is worth noting, as Jantsch has pointed out, that collaborative and cooperative international R & D activity has hitherto 'been conceived mainly in an economic framework'.[16] One can predict with some confidence that if Jantsch's advice were followed, and this 'narrow framework' abandoned for a wider one, embracing what he calls 'social development at large', then it might well follow that technology as economics would spill over into technology as politics.

Having put forward this interpretation, almost as it were in parenthesis, one can now return to the general literature. Assuming that the states concerned elect to continue together, then, according to Lindberg: Economic integration can be expected to have political consequences if it leads to the development of central institutions and policies, if the tasks assigned to these institutions are important enough to concern major groups in the society, if these tasks are quite specific, and if the tasks are inherently expansive.[17]

Acknowledging the dismal failure of Euratom, Lindberg and Scheingold have argued more recently that, 'on the level of theory', there now exist sound reasons for believing that the problems typical of it could, 'in the current atmosphere of urgency and in the broader bargaining contexts being proposed', be overcome. In their view: 'A wide range of political action is available. Redistributive outcomes seem possible and everybody stands to gain. No single nation will predominate in all areas, and extensive logrolling and side-payments should be possible as the prime mechanism of coalition building.'[18]

Is this perhaps slightly wishful thinking? Those who think so may also find themselves agreeing with Sewell that 'the most desirable route to international community building proceeds gradually from initial problems,'[19] and still have doubts about the future of technological collaboration, on the grounds that it is not easy to arrange that acts of technological collaboration meet the corresponding tests, said by him to be political neutrality, specificity of focus and separateness from each other and from potentially rival activities. In this context one remembers again that European governments have often not only, or even primarily, been concerned with eliminating a 'technological gap' between Europe and the United States, so much as with eliminating gaps of all sorts between themselves.

Sanwald and Stohler write in praise of the imbalances arising out of economic cooperation: 'the positive aspect of partial integration is therefore its inner dynamics which tend unambiguously to an overall integration. Only complete integration will remove the disequilibrium between the integrated and the remaining sectors.'[20]

The point is underlined by Scitovsky[21] when he speaks of 'the increased scope for the deliberate allocation of Western European industrial capacity as a conscious policy aimed at compensating countries for losses suffered in other fields'.[22] As a simple example of the pressure caused by disequilibrium, one might mention the papers presented to the EEC Commission by a group of major European aircraft firms in 1970 and 1971, calling among other things for assistance in overcoming differential cost escalation, and compensation for the effects of parity changes. On the other hand, one is bound to question whether the totality of European commitments in technological collaboration has really as yet been great enough for the undeniable disequilibria to have had more than marginal spill-over effects. And, so far as conscious compensation is concerned, Wallich puts the main point very bluntly: 'Most of us deplore the view of developing countries that each of them should have its steel mill. The same surely applies to computer manufacture . . . [but] one cannot fight emotions with statistics'.[23]

Of the dimensions of political integration identified by Nye, European technological collaboration might be said to contain elements of two, what he calls, 'policy' and 'attitudinal' integration,[24] though given the evident limits to the European awareness of common dilemmas and mutual obligations, as manifested, for example, in a continuing strong willingness to collaborate as separate nations with the United States, it is more policy than attitudinal integration that has so far occurred. Using Nye's indices, although there has been collaboration or cooperation in several scientific and technological sectors, the overall *scope* remains narrow. Second, only in aerospace has its *extent* been substantial, and even there, except for the post-Plowden period in Britain, collaboration has almost exclusively been dictated by the piecemeal defence of national positions. Finally, the general socio-political *salience* of collaborative ventures has mostly been low, with the Tripartite Project, the MRCA, Concorde and the European airbus as the most notable (potential) exceptions. Kaiser's[25] phrase 'multi-bureaucratic decision-making' fits many of these technological involvements very well. As he says, such devices as the unanimity rule and the ritual assertion of maintained sovereignty conceal the fact that 'national bureaucracies from several countries jointly allocate substantial resources in a process of negotiation and mutual adjustment which is mostly hidden from the public'. It all seems a long way from his 'multinational integration' and true 'transnational politics'.

The fundamental difficulty in trying to assess the value of technological collaboration in promoting political integration has in effect been spelled out by Haas: 'judgements as to whether co-operation is "successful" must be based on criteria very different from those appropriate to the study of integration.'[26] Of particular relevance, one suspects, to technological collaboration is Schmitter's concept of 'self-encapsulation' which Haas quotes: 'Many fields of potentially integrative activity, after successful accomplishment, result in "self-encapsulation" organisationally and attitudinally and therefore may not contribute to the evolution of new demands by actors.'[27]

'Self-encapsulation' evidently has technological consequences as well. How, for example, could one operationalise Belassa's[28] distinction between induced technological change, the kind which follows directly an increase in market size, and autonomous technological change, where the connection is at most indirect through research expenditures, when one considers cases like Concorde or DRAGON, where, apart from the difficulties of attributing a meaning to the term 'market', one also has substantial technical 'self-encapsulation' ?

In this context, Nau has made a notably brave attempt to test some of the hypotheses associated with the theoretical concept of 'interdependence' against the European record in fast breeder reactor cooperation. His first observation is that, instead of the heightened salience of technical issues leading to 'a new genre of cooperative politics', in the case of fast breeder reactors in 1961-2, 'In an inversion of functionalist logic, political changes created the conditions for overcoming scientific and technological differences'.

His second finding is hardly less damaging. Instead of inter-dependence enhancing the importance of functional specialisation, 'interdependence may itself be a function of specialisation which, in turn may be a function of political agreement'. Nor is Nau much happier with the hypotheses that increasing interdependence requires more regulatory mechanisms and institutions, and makes it harder to maintain 'qualitatively unequal' relations. His overall conclusion is striking: 'The above discussion suggests nothing more than that the assumptions and hypotheses of interdependence retain a limited utility in the analysis of European civil nuclear relations. Judging from the difficulties of cooperation in other sectors of technology, this conclusion may also hold for European technological relations in general. Beyond this speculation takes over.'[29]

Skolnikoff's opinion is that, while the pooling of technological capabilities may in some cases contribute to political integration, 'in most instances it will more likely result only in increased co-operation – and interdependence – between sovereign states'.[30] In similar low key, Wright sees advanced technology as no longer being centre stage, so that it is likely in the seventies to be neither a catalyst nor a symbol for initiatives leading to European political unity. Yet he feels that selected technologies 'may now come into their own as critical testing areas for the capacity of European nations and industrial organisations to create and participate in more highly evolved systems of organised activity', everything perhaps depending on 'open, informed and timely assessment of technology-related programmes'.[31]

One critical question is clearly whether the process of integration benefits even from unsuccessful collaboration, in that even this is integrative activity and integrative activity may feed on itself.[32] *Nature*, for example, has suggested that 'Already there are signs that the successes have done more good than the failures have done harm'.[33] And as a second example, Feld concludes from his study of transnational business collaboration among the Six that, although it 'cannot be regarded as very auspicious', certain of its byproducts hold promise, so that, while the process may be 'extremely slow', and while 'there may well be flaws in the neo-functionalist hypotheses', nevertheless such collaboration does illustrate 'the continuing potential force of functionalism for the transformation of a regional system'.[34]

Among the factors which Feld stresses are the right choice of partners, recognition of the differences in government-industry relations, and the need to overcome the vested interests of the national bureaucracies. Von Lilienstern, distinguishing a spectrum of intensity in international business agreements, adds: 'Cooperation signifies a *dialogue between partners of equal standing and the eventual conversion of competitors into associates* . . . The main condition for success is the human element.'[35]

Taking a concrete example of technological collaboration, the Martel project, the importance has been greatly stressed of 'the fact that the people concerned recognised that neither they nor their juniors were perfect collaborators'.[36] It is worth noting too that people involved even in very 'end-oriented' collaborative projects like this often claim a deeper 'means' significance for them, as a few other examples will show:[37]

> the great lesson of Concorde . . . [is] that collaboration does work . . . Concorde will be remembered as one of the first and one of the greatest symbols of . . . [Europe's] joint endeavours.

> We are convinced that we are clearing the ground for the generations to come. These, it may be trusted, will be brought up with a more open mind towards European cooperation. [said of the Anglo-French helicopter package].

> One does have the feeling that in working with what it seems now wrong to call foreigners, one is doing a little in the strange mode of a military aircraft to unite Europe, if you want to put a name to it, and bring people together. [Said of the MRCA].

In the less materialist scientific realm, Piganiol had earlier argued that 'A European scientific community is a prerequisite for the emergence of a European mind and outlook', and King has stressed that 'European science with its long tradition is an essential element in the construction of the new Europe.'[38] It is perhaps not stretching the point too far to see here a link with the ideas of Deutsch.

It does not follow, of course, that one should extrapolate any of these examples to the point where a collaborative project not justifiable on criteria of cost-effectiveness, scientific excellence or social need becomes automatically acceptable on grounds of the goodwill likely to be generated. It is fascinating on exactly this point to note the recent outline by Ingrey of the current British philosophy of collaboration in so far as military equipment is concerned. Ingrey fully recognises the 'almost idealistic charisma' which surrounds collaboration and cooperation, and he has a shrewd perception too both of the political mileage which this is worth, and of the drawbacks which idealism can entail. He believes that the British 'step by step, pragmatic approach' is 'the only sensible one'. To be 'realistic', collaboration must be voluntary, be predicated on mutual interest and coincidence of situations, and reflect approximately equal budgetary resources and development capabilities. Collaboration is 'an important *but not the only efficient method of procurement*'. Ingrey acknowledges the weakness of this appraisal, but reckons that 'more ambitious and radical policies' – involving perhaps a European Common Market in defence equipment or a European Defence Procurement Agency – would, because the necessary political and technical foundation is, in his opinion, lacking, lead to 'artificial distortions'.[39] The political glamour of collaboration is welcome in other words, but only if it complements an otherwise logical policy option.

The safest assumption is evidently that scientific and technological collaboration needs to march pretty closely in step with other moves towards economic and political integration if it is to realise fully its own potential in this respect. Unless one argues along the lines indicated above, to the effect that the build-up of collaborative momentum is both steady, subtle and a bridge from 'low' to 'high' politics, then the corollary is that as an isolated element its integrative potential must be strictly limited. If this in turn is accepted, it would follow that when, for example, Armand and Drancourt complain that collaboration has been carried out 'in a spirit of contract, not cooperation', and when they call for 'special commissions . . . to promote European operations in new sectors of economic activity', it is not really enough for them to argue that 'the thrust of technical progress makes structural adaptation essential'. The last thing they, and commentators like them, intend is that exhortations in favour of structural adaptation, or the creation of new institutions, should lead only to structural adaptation and the creation of new institutions.[40]

It is, to be sure, impossible to disguise in European technological collaboration a 'complete absence of homogeneity' ('a Chinese puzzle in which all the components have only one thing in common, that they are in a state of crisis'[41]), and it would be particularly ironical if one had in European industry and technology converging functional interests which were not transitory, but which were none the less frustrated by the structural framework of European decision-making.[42] Yet new institutions in this general field, as a recent Unesco report observes, are costly and of doubtful utility. As it says, 'in many cases international scientific and technological cooperation has had very little connexion with the needs of national economic and social development . . . there should be a strengthening of the links between scientific and technological cooperation on the one hand and economic cooperation at the various levels . . . on the other.'[43]

The solution to problems at the national level is frequently the creation of new bodies, and quite often such bodies manage rapidly to develop both personality and power. By contrast, each new body created at the European level has constantly to work hard to avoid being discredited. It is not that new, or for that matter old, European-level institutions in this field are unimportant, simply that, on the evidence, they are always in danger of becoming substitutes for policies agreed between governments which would commit those governments to a scheme of cooperative incentives, which, as a prime objective, encouraged the cooperative involvement of non-governmental and quasi-governmental actors, and which expanded in their ambition as political integration proceeded.

VIII Some Lessons

Creating Commitment

This interim analysis of European technological collaboration has been concerned with questions of commitment, process, control and evaluation, the ideas of equity, efficiency and accountability having also been introduced. These headings were largely derived from the subject matter itself, but they do in turn seem to lead to some useful insights.

Of all the political problems associated with European technological collaboration it is inevitable that the clutch of difficulties associated with the securing of an initial commitment to joint action should be seen as the most revealing and fundamental. If European technical projects are arranged in order of the difficulty experienced in building commitment then broadly the spectrum runs from scientific projects at one end, through conventional military products, to civil technological ventures, with military nuclear collaboration the non-existent extension at the other end. The costs associated with much of high energy physics and scientific space research in particular are such that if no programme is mounted at the European level, and, increasingly, at the fully international level, then progress, if it remains possible at all, becomes severely limited. What is more, the technical community involved is an unusually transnational one, so that a wide range of difficulties can be ironed out prior to government involvement. Of no other part of the 'collaboration spectrum' can it be said, at least as yet, that such vested interests as exist tend with growing frequency to see their best hopes in collaborative action.[1] Even on occasion in this sector, and without exception in all others, technological collaboration encounters, it has been shown, a range of difficulties, some real, some spurious, and embodying commitment in a specific organisation does not necessarily eradicate them.

In line with this are the impressions set out by Professor Bondi, for some years Director-General of ESRO, and currently Chief Scientific Adviser to the Ministry of Defence, regarding the problems which beset an intergovernmental body concerned with technical objectives. Bondi dismisses as a 'pseudo problem' the task of building multinational professional teams, and feels that the geographical spread of industry is a much worse problem for Americans than for Europeans. He has little more sympathy for *juste retour* problems, but considers that this is a matter of persuading industry, through a concentration on multinational funding, to group in consortia, a process requiring special encouragement, he says, in the case of small nations, and also very determined attempts to prevent all companies from seeking to acquire all specialisations. Two problems of international decision-making give him more pause for thought, namely the 'uncorrelated periods of paralysis' due to each of perhaps ten governments being for some fifteen to twenty per cent of the time involved in elections, government reshuffles or extraneous crises, and the fact that national policies may become an almost accidental outcome of the particular choice of technical advisers. Beyond these problems again, on his interpretation, are the 'genuine divergences', based on which industries the various countries wish to promote, and on how much money they wish to spend at any given time.[2]

To the extent, in particular, that collaboration requires or implies permanent European industrial links, one dare not underestimate the intellectual complexity, commercial complications and political difficulties which lie in the way of their establishment. And it would probably be wise to regard legal, tax and financial problems not simply as themselves the real obstructions, but more as symptoms of a much deeper socio-psychological uncertainty which political positions are bound to reflect. The industrial and technological policies of European governments demonstrate above all a continuing attachment to national solutions. Even as these are presented they are frequently acknowledged to be sub-optimum arrangements pending 'European' solutions at some indeterminate future date. One is reminded of the differential equation which may have a transient as well as a steady-state solution, either one of them in particular circumstances being the most significant. On one view, the steady-state solution for Europe would consist of integrated transnational industrial units, paralleled by common governmental procurement policies, the whole being concerted politically by appropriate supranational institutions in the best interests of the European population as a whole. The transient solution would then refer to the intermediate stage, during which political and commercial bargaining would determine in each industrial technology the long-term pecking order. Technological collaboration to date can in fact be seen as part of this transient phase. The scope for commercial and political argument and bitterness is obviously very great during this process, and one recalls that transient solutions to differential equations are the only ones of real interest in those circumstances where they lead to serious impairment of the system they describe. To illustrate the simile, many lamps burn brightly, provided that they do not fuse when first switched on.

Currently, the process of commitment, though hopefully benefiting from a constructive cooperative spirit, remains a combination of techno-economic analysis, diplomatic negotiation and legal drafting exercise. Clear and detailed articles of agreement do not ensure a successful collaboration, nor their absence prevent it, but they do tend to remove one of the thorniest problems over which the partners may later fall out. Two other interesting questions with respect to commitment concern the source of the original initiative and the distinction, if any, to be drawn between 'programme' and 'project' commitments.

Broadly, the initiative may come either from producer interests, usually private firms, presumably aware of 'potential', from user interests, the armed services, the airlines, the electricity generating boards, the physicists and so on, presumably aware of 'need', or from government itself, in the sense of politicians, officials or research organisations. Government naturally has motives of its own, one of them normally being its own appreciation of the need-potential equation. In the still rare instances where multinational groups of producers and users are able to arrive at a joint initiative, the task of government is straightforward; essentially it has only to decide to what extent, if at all, the resulting proposal is worthy of public financial support. When the initiative comes from only one of the two, government must additionally act as broker. When the initiative is primarily national, whether from producers, users, or from within government itself, a third function falls to government, that of producing a more or less artificial transnational desire for the product or facility concerned, and for collaboration. It is a reasonable objection that few real cases fall exactly into any one of these three categories. The counter to this is that most cases have elements of the third, and it is in this situation that the task of government is most complex and the probability of good decisions lowest.

Beaton had some thoughts along related lines:

> One of the strangest and most persistent ideas to come out of the British end of the European movement is the notion that a united Europe can most easily be launched through advanced technology ... Having failed to see the need for a structure capable of making incredibly difficult industrial and invest-ment decisions at home, the Government was unlikely to understand this basic weakness in its European plans.[3]

Mr Wedgwood Benn in fact thought that his Ministry had begun a new and hard-headed commercial approach:

> At first the impact of Mintech thinking on European science ministers was profoundly shocking and was taken as an indica-tion that Britain had lost interest in European cooperation ... But ... European ministers and their officials came to recognise that this philosophy ... made a lot of sense.[4]

If an environment can be created in which producers and users are encouraged through formal and informal arrangements to agree amongst themselves on 'need' and – or 'potential', then it is likely not only that government will have one instead of two or three major tasks to perform, but also that the achievement of a good balance between efficiency and equity later will be facilitated by initiative-phase commercial and industrial bargaining, thereby minimising commitment-phase political negotiation. This is also likely to be the simplest route to permanent European industrial and commercial links. One might in addition expect it to facilitate the meshing of defence requirements, though here political considerations are bound to remain paramount.

The Scope and Nature of Collaboration

It is suggested, then, that collaborative plans, especially for com-mercial or quasi-commercial technology, which originate at the political (national government) or technocratic (supranational authority) levels require in general to be viewed with particular caution. But there is a class of technology to which this reservation cannot fairly be applied, namely that class which includes products whose development, utilisation or application yields as much a public as a private return or which are otherwise judged desirable on broader social grounds. Here there is great scope for both politicians and technocrats, if only because technological imperatives express themselves, *via* interest and professional groups, much more readily as demands for military, commercial or scientific equipment than for this sort of socially-orientated technology. Since the EEC Commission has, so far at least, been denied the competence to frame policies, as opposed to proposals, in the industrial and technological fields at large, this might also, as the Commission has shown signs of recognising, prove the least sensitive sector in which to create and then expand that competence. More generally, collaboration might in practice prove easiest to compass and strengthen in the case of technologies and industries which are still nascent rather than fully established.[5]

This is also the place to note that even as regards commercial technology there is probably much more scope for collaboration than has yet been demonstrated in 'small' as opposed to 'big' technology. 'Small' technology is not always 'advanced', but then neither is 'big' technology. It is simply that the producers and users of big technology are generally better placed to secure government support, leading if necessary to international collaboration. There remain very many industries and technologies where the possibilities of collaboration have received little serious attention and many where they have not been appreciated at all. The pressures have nearly all come from the 'advanced' sectors, but major problems of rationalisation, reorganisation, re-equipment or redirection remain in the 'older' sectors, such a shipbuilding, steel and the motor industry, and in other sectors of private industry too. Private collaborative activity in Europe could possibly with public advantage be much richer than it is.[6] This need not necessarily be at the expense of government-level collaboration, nor on the other hand need the outcome in every case be the proliferation of ever larger semi-sovereign corporations. With or without collaboration the giant corporation is a creature of the times, and there is no denying that it may pose new and very taxing problems for contemporary government. But, as with all new challenges, governments must learn, preferably in concert, to master the problems and amplify the very real advantages. Shunning collaboration may delay the era of the indigenous supercorporation in Europe, but it is just as likely to encourage the expansion there of other corporate groups even less under European control.

Returning to the second question mentioned above, the distinction between 'programmes' and 'projects', a basic point is that organisations entrusted with programmes normally have greater opportunities than those entrusted only with specific projects for acquiring a momentum of their own (cf. ESRO and ELDO). Provided this momentum is directed towards objectives which governments broadly support (ESRO), or about which they care little (CERN), then all may be well. Otherwise (Euratom), the task of such organisations can become an impossible one. An additional requirement in the creation of such bodies needs therefore to be agreement on an unequivocal equation relating continuity and control. Supranational organisations charged with executing a programme need continuity; governments must have means of exercising control. Extremely thorough organisation and programme reviews, which are regular but not too frequent, and which allow for unilateral withdrawal, are likely to offer as good an answer as any. Governments must have the right, and from time to time some must be expected to take advantage of it, to withdraw; but preferably only under very carefully delineated circumstances. This is also, of course, tantamount to saying in the end that collaboration is best on an *à la carte* basis. There may be circumstances when governments are prepared to commit themselves to more than this, but the justification for *à la carte* commitments, as regards not only projects but also projects within programmes, is that if certain governments are not persuaded that a project is desirable on its own merits, are unwilling to bow to the moral pressure to join in from those governments which wish to mount that project and find no value in yielding for the sake of some advantage elsewhere, then it is hard to see what end is attained by trying to compel them. Collaboration that is not voluntary is not doomed, but it needs to be more than ordinarily successful if it is to overcome the handicap.[7]

To return to the simile used above, the long-term, or as it was called there, the steady-state solution, for European technological collaboration, involving, as it presumably would, substantial industrial and commercial integration, necessarily appeals most to the technocrat. He is distressed, even appalled, by the duplication and inefficiency he regards as anachronistically characteristic of contemporary Europe, and wherever and whenever he believes he has found a 'think small, think national' attitude he seeks to combat it with a 'think big, think continental' plan. He knows quite well that the short term, or 'transient' solutions – 'fixes' might be a better word – for Europe's problems will almost invariably be politically determined. But it is also true that in this situation technocratic exhortation is itself a political reference point, and to be taken seriously it is therefore imperative that it be realistic as well as ambitious. If the technocrat can get no power behind the stick, he must be sure to make the carrot irresistible.

As in the case of commitment, so also in those of process and control; again there are technocratic as well as democratic considerations. To begin with, the organisational and administrative arrangements for collaboration are not, it must be remembered, simply static monuments to those problems solved, and those left unsolved, in the mobilisation of commitment. On the contrary, they contain within themselves the dynamic causes of future stresses, both managerial and political. One might add that on the difference between Euratom and Panavia rests not only the success of the original programme or project, but also the contribution of whatever is accomplished to the general momentum of collaboration. The example may be unsound as well as unkind – Euratom is not dead and Panavia may yet disappoint – but the principle itself is much harder to challenge.

Three of the concepts identified in the stages of process and control are especially important. Taking together equity, efficiency and accountability, the first and last are very political in their overtones, while efficiency is rather more immediately a technocratic aim. Furthermore, equity must pre-eminently be a national concern, efficiency a supranational one, while accountability, ideally, ought to be both. The three are certainly very different objectives, not mutually incompatible, but rather in permanent competition with each other, and one might therefore wish responsibility for ensuring them in any given case to be placed with three quite separate institutions. For example, had the EEC real political power in its own right, then the three institutions concerned could respectively be the Council, the Commission and the Parliament. Such an assignment of responsibilities is, of course, not likely to be easily or quickly forthcoming, and in the meanwhile it is easy to understand the confusion which can arise in non-EEC collaboration, where equity and efficiency are usually sought by the same agency, a government department, and in EEC cooperation, where the unequal distribution of power has seriously limited the pursuit of efficiency by Euratom. In both cases, it is especially unfortunate that true accountability is rendered, if at all, only incidentally.

Accountability and the Public Interest

One surely cannot emphasise too much the significance of accountability in contemporary government, either generally or with specific regard to technology.[8] The goal of widespread participation is a worthy, but also an illusory one. The concerns of government are many and multiplying, their complexity great and growing, and citizens in general have neither the time nor the expertise to maintain their position with relation to bureaucracy. (Or traditional civil servants, perhaps, to maintain theirs with respect to the members of what Galbraith has chosen to call the technostructure.) And even if increased leisure assists in one respect and better technically oriented education in another, what method exists to increase the interest and ability of the individual in regard to those public issues which seem technically remote or whose consequences impact on him only broadly? Enhanced participation in organisations or policy-making activities whose impact is specific is one thing, though even then it is often forgotten that the interests must also be protected of those others affected who do not choose, or still lack the means, to participate. But participation is a limited instrument in the case of policies whose effect is general, and which therefore usually concern large sections of, or the whole of, the national community, a category which embraces the products of advanced technology.

Participation is perhaps not quite the red herring which some commentators have on occasion suggested, more the pink elephant of the morning after, the morning after the troubles of 1968 that is. Accountability, on the other hand, is potentially a much more potent device for securing good government. The theoretical motivation of representative and responsible government is a constancy of will to act in the public interest. But the public interest is much too nebulous to be detected for in the detailed policies of government. A more practical position is to ask that government be accountable – defining a truly accountable government to be one bound to furnish the public or the public's representatives with as full a report of its doings as the public or the representatives may require, the onus lying with government to prove its case if it seeks to withhold information in what it takes to be the national interest. Accountability would then rest on the wide availability of detailed information. Putting this comparatively, the more accountable a government, the more open would be all its activities to public inspection, and the right to call to account would then be recognised as an essential check on both weak decision-making and on technocracy.

But how is one to apply this concept in the case of European joint activities in the technical and industrial field? As a first point, since the consequences of technology are now unquestionably major sources of political activity, there is every reason to press for governments to be fully accountable for their actions in stimulating, controlling and utilising technology itself. And what applies to governments should obviously apply with no less force to intergovernmental organisations. It is all the more disturbing, then, to find the compilers of a recent study of European intergovernmental scientific and technical organisations having cause to criticise the excessive confidentiality practised by certain of these bodies. In terms of the requirements of accountable government such an attitude by intergovernmental bodies is, as these authors say, 'utterly indefensible',[9] and one remembers that a virtue claimed for CERN, easily the most successful of them, has been the 'general principle of no secrecy'[10] which it has sought to apply.

Unfortunately, even with regard to policies which operate only at the national level, most parliaments are, or have allowed themselves to become, very blunt instruments for securing accountability. But even were they much more capable than they are, national parliaments could not be expected to approach joint activities with the appropriate set of criteria, because they define the public interest, as they must, with reference to the national community. And this becomes progressively more inadequate as collaboration gives way to cooperation and cooperation to integration. To put the argument in concrete form, there is no need for a special bilateral institution to obtain accountability for the British and American public money and guarantees involved in the RB211 engine and the Tristar aircraft. The American Congress and the British Parliament are, or should be, up to the task. One might perhaps have said the same initially of Concorde, but the more collaboration there is, the more it begins to resemble cooperation, and the more necessary it becomes to take a supranational view. When they think of the subject at all, European governments mostly tend to regard a genuine parliamentary institution at the European level as at some indefinite stage complementing their own European policy-making activities. The net result from the British point of view is that accountability at the national level for the country's collaborative involvements is less satisfactory even than for comparable national activities, and there is no compensating European-level accountability.[11]

This argument for an effective parliamentary device to pursue accountability at the European level is predicted on the assumption that joint technical and industrial involvement will gradually multiply and expand. But parallel cases have been or can be made out with respect to other areas of policy, and the total argument is really the sum of all these, though with the case developed here perhaps especially strong, given that no matter what cooperative gear the Community is driven in, technology and industry together must form the prime motor of Europe's advance, if advance there is to be.

It is not suggested that a 'genuine' parliamentary institution or an 'effective' parliamentary device necessarily presupposes direct elections. In the industrial and technological fields it seems most promising to ask that the parliamentary body be given in the first place real powers over cooperative and then collaborative programmes. If such a grant of power to the European body were both real and substantial, then the demand for direct representation would be likely to become irresistible, but so long as the power granted continues to be neither real nor substantial, then the demand for direct representation remains irrelevant.[12]

Evaluation and the Real Objectives of Collaboration

For all collaborative projects, indeed for *all* projects, full retrospective evaluation is a good deal more important than it is usually made to seem. It is quite true that the affairs of the moment press hard, but there must be retrospective analysis if learning is to be based on science rather than folklore. And in making an evaluation of the kind called for here it is also important to distinguish satisfactorily between evaluation of results against original objectives, and evaluation against expectations evolved *en route*. Some of the general questions which require *post facto* to be answered are obvious:

1. Was the collaborative objective defined the most appropriate one, was it pursued efficiently and is the result or product as successful as it might have been?
2. Did the organisation and management methods permit sufficient accountability in all applicable senses of that word?
3. Were the changes in the capabilities of the programme contributors as a result of the collaboration internationally equitable, and were profits, losses, extramural costs, etc. incident fairly?

Other questions will depend on the nature of the project. Politicians, officials and members of legislatures could be expected to place rather different emphases on these questions, though the distinction is much less clear-cut than with the original concepts of equity, efficiency and accountability. In particular, ministers and parliamentarians will forgive much more if a project is an evident success. It may be added that a retrospective analysis is properly regarded as an integral part of a project; one might therefore press for publication of its results with as much detail as possible and accept recriminations as the price of progress.

It must be admitted that recriminations will in any case normally be heightened by the fact that governments typically view collaboration more as a means than as an end, and the effective end to which it is then a means is not always one which can be openly admitted. Within the European Community the nominal end is long-term integration, variously construed. Indeed, it is in recognition of this that the term 'cooperation' has been used in this book for Community programmes, in contradistinction to 'collaboration', retained for cases where the overt end itself theoretically dominates. But both within the Community and without, governments almost invariably have other, and more national, tactical and strategic ends in mind than the overt one, so that cooperation or collaboration comes to be regarded as, for instance, a means of keeping the Americans out, of strengthening the national capability or of preventing an unfavourable collaborative development between other European nations. The integrative potential of technology must as a result be assessed against the fact that the technological field is, or can be, particularly suitable for the furtherance of other and more general foreign policy objectives.

Gilpin has demonstrated this in detail in the case of Gaullist France.[13] He begins by referring to the Gaullist rejection of federal European policies on the grounds of the inevitable domination of an unavoidably weak united Europe by the United States. Joint international action in science and technology, like all other such joint action, then remains a matter for sovereign states, and Gilpin finds that French policy in this sphere has had 'the earmarks of traditional balance of power politics', namely the search for international agreements to balance American power, and the pursuit of primacy within those agreements. Gilpin also denies that French policy in this sector has been wholly chauvinistic, arguing that 'paradoxically her policy is the most internationalist, as well as the most nationalist' of any European state. France, on this interpretation, has seen the need both for international programmes to supplement national ones, and for vigorous national programmes to take full advantage of the international ones. Gilpin's opinion is that this sort of strategy lessens the 'effective use' of Europe's resources, and he does not consider either, that France can continue indefinitely to 'have it both ways'.

There would seem, in theory at least, to be one weakness in this last argument, even overlooking the fact that French policy has not consistently demonstrated the high level of internal logic implied here, and allowing also that in the very long run Gilpin may be right in insisting that to meet the total challenge of technical change France must, as he puts it, 'cease to be France'. The weakness lies in the fact that French policies of the kind identified by Gilpin in principle could improve, and in practice have improved, France's technical standing, and therefore to some extent her political bargaining power with respect to her European partners. It follows that, even if France is eventually compelled by circumstances to accept more consciously 'European' policies, she could be in a much stronger position to do this than would have been the case had she from the outset settled for such an approach.

It is as well to recognise then, that technological collaboration, far from promoting integration, could without goodwill lead to the reverse. Output imbalances from collaboration are tolerable only over the short term, or where net national advantage is more important than comparative international advantage. In general, one can only ask that governments consider most carefully whether in any given case it is worth 'dishing the French' or the British or the West Germans or for that matter the Americans, at the possible expense of their own longer term interests. Unfortunately, it is no doubt the case that those concerned with the political dimension of technological collaboration have very mixed ideas about what exactly they want of it. Governments as well as individuals are frequently content to travel hopefully, happy that the ultimate destination reveal itself only gradually. Nor should such pragmatism necessarily be entirely disparaged, provided that its limitations are understood. And one of them is increased uncertainty about the relationship between short-term choices and long-term interests. There seems to be no virtue in putting forward here yet another 'programme' or 'plan' for Europe's technological future – the preference only of the author. On the contrary, this book's concern with the future is more exploratory than normative, to borrow the terminology of the futurologists. But this one normative element does seem worth stressing, the need for just a little more strategic clarity.[14]

Some Unconventional Alternatives

The attempt has also been made here to follow mostly orthodox lines, but it is right that the unorthodox should at this point receive some brief mention. One might, or one might not, wish to defend the following three intellectual positions, and in any case detailed consideration of them does not properly belong in the present analysis, which, in effect, treats as axiomatic principles which they most seriously question. The third one in particular is related to the 'Swedish route solutions' which it was said in the first chapter were too fundamental to be discussed in this book at the length which some would feel they deserve. Cumulatively, or even separately, the three arguments suggest a very different and a very unconventional philosophy. They concern respectively the economic characteristics of high technology, the role of government in general with respect to big technological projects and the role specifically of the British Government in the context of collaboration. Wild makes the first point succinctly and controversially: 'it would appear that in some projects the development cost may no longer be really justifiable in terms of either economic advantage for commercial products or cost-effectiveness for military items.' Asymptotic development costs, ever smaller gains for ever higher costs, Wild regards as typical of any technical effort.[15]

The second point is made equally controversially in a recent OECD report.[16] This questions whether large technological programmes of any kind are necessary for vigorous national performance, arguing that they may well constitute in general a misallocation of resources, and that government involvement can lead to 'the development of "pure technology", beyond either the capabilities of the industrial structure or the requirements of the market'.

Underlying these first two quotations is a yet more fundamental point which needs to be brought out. It concerns the degree to which, even excluding the possibly ill-advised public financial support of technology implied by this OECD report, technical change is 'out of control'. There is a case, subscribed to by many, that the whole phenomenon of organised innovation, the core dynamic of industrial society, creates new problems about as fast as, or faster than, it helps to solve old ones. How serious a matter is this? One can argue that such problems are themselves capable of scientific solution, and that eventually technical development will not precipitate difficulties of comparable gravity. Or one can argue that the very essence of technical change as it is experienced and prosecuted by man consists in riding the wind, that is, discovering new solutions for old problems while simultaneously creating new ones. Then there is the third view, that contemporary technology is irredeemably corrupt and that its ills in the long run will outweigh its benefits. The numbers of those who hold this opinion, though possibly growing, are still small; their most constructive response is the development of what has come to be called 'alternative technology'.

There is obviously a vital issue here but it cannot be pursued in this book which is based on the assumption that, despite respectable academic argument, and the observations of a number of politicians, economic growth is unlikely in the near future to be displaced in Western Europe as a, if not the, principle criterion of successful government. And it is in the context of this assumption that technological collaboration becomes a policy option. Within it too there arises the third, and most directly provocative, of the three unorthodox arguments referred to above, Bellamy's view of technological collaboration by Britain with European partners.[17] Instead of the 'apparent impossibilities' of national production and the 'costly uncertainties' of joint production he offers a 'clear and logical' alternative:

> Other wealthier or more foolish countries should be allowed to take the risks of aerospace development and production and we should buy from them . . . In addition we should engage ourselves where possible in collaborative advanced technology projects *but as a junior partner* . . . and such collaboration should not necessarily be restricted to Europe.

Bellamy believes that Britain could thus gain access to almost all the technology of a collaborative project for a very small financial stake. A small and wholly national R & D competence would be retained, 'principally for reasons of morale', and Britain should not try to incorporate her own equipment in products purchased abroad simply to keep her remaining aerospace work-force employed.

Bellamy's position is usually challenged first, by stressing the strategic significance, in either the commercial or the national security sense, of industries such as aviation, and second, by pointing to the psychological damage and economic penalties, including balance of payments ones, involved either in running down a major industry or in failing to maintain it in the van of technical progress. But while Bellamy may be wrong, and while Britain may blame herself too much for a real or imagined lack of technological and industrial success, it remains hard to deny that her policies in respect of technology have frequently been arrived at in a rather haphazard way. Of course, it is impossible for ministers, or even for governments, always to wipe the slate clean and build up policy from first principles; the inheritance from the past generally leaves very little scope for such really independent choice. But perhaps there can still be fairly stable and reasonably long term guidelines, whose disciplinary significance might be enhanced rather than diminished when, as must sometimes happen, ministers choose or feel constrained to depart from them. It must be admitted, though, that the inherent financial and organisational 'lumpiness' of projects like Concorde, the RB211 engine or the Advanced Gas Cooled Reactor ensures that the evolution of a strategy for technology will not be a smooth and incremental process.

Prospects for Britain and for Europe

In theory, the basic strategic guidelines would presumably refer to the preferred direction of policy and to the extent and form of government financial support. There are broadly four policy options normally open to government in any given case: refuse to take any initiative or to provide any assistance; favour one of perhaps several possible national solutions; seek the most nationally satisfactory European scheme; or look for a wider international arrangement. As was explained in the first chapter, British governments, of both political parties, it seems now rule out the first of these, if only because support is thought to be desirable to offset that received by competing foreign concerns from their own governments. As between the other three policy options, examples of each exist or have existed – fast breeder reactors (national solution), aviation, post-Plowden (European dependence), RB211 (American link) – but in many cases one cannot feel fully confident that either the direction of policy or the level of financial support has always been the outcome of logical consistency and critical scrutiny.

Membership of the EEC will not of itself solve, or even necessarily transform, such problems as Britain has, or believes she has, in the industrial and technological field. They will begin to be changed if the Community becomes, as Britain must demand, as much an industrial structure as it has been an agricultural one. But even then there can be no totally efficacious external nostrum for internal difficulties. And Britain's difficulties, by no means confined to her, but perhaps manifesting themselves in a more than usually intractable form in her case, for a variety of reasons, are those of deciding upon, and having decided upon, building an industrial structure and a machinery of choice appropriate to her international economic, and to a lesser extent political, position. The act of choosing and the business of implementation are not, in spite of technology's dependence on the state, matters only for government. They are best accepted as some of the natural, if complex, questions typical of contemporary politics in industrial society. And if this is so there needs to be a wider and better-informed discussion of the proper role in the British context of the 'advanced' technology industries, of the 'older' technology industries, and of the 'lower' technology industries. The relationship between the state and technology needs to be one of healthy symbiosis, not of doubtful parasitism. This has not been a central concern of the present book but there have been encouraging signs in recent years that a constructive debate is emerging, as well as some evidence of hysteria. In such a setting the new European dimension of policy can be one of promise, so long as it is not expected to substitute for an effective blend in British Government of technical entrepreneurship and social responsibility.

This book has also mostly avoided the question of whether or not European governments and companies 'should' or 'should not' collaborate with non-European ones, American ones presently and perhaps increasingly the Japanese. It has done so because whether or not they *should*, for some time to come at least they surely *will* whenever they judge it to be in their own best interests. Ultimately one's views on this must depend on how one ranks the objective of European integration. There are real dangers in the modern world in trying to build walls around countries or continents, but one does not have to be by any means a committed European to observe that the governments of Europe have much work to do if they are to strengthen the centrapetal incentives between themselves to co-operate and weaken the centrifugal temptations. It is obviously even more premature to conjecture at present about the possibilities of East-West collaboration in European industry and technology, but it would be shortsighted to presume that such opportunities will not occur, or to assume that they will always and necessarily be of marginal significance if they do.

From all that has been said here the task of the EEC Commission would seem to be a very unenviable one. Having identified what it judges to be in the best European interest it has little alternative but to pursue this. On the other hand, national governments and their official advisers have a duty to hold fast to what they consider to be their separate national interests. Since every sign suggests that the path from collaboration to cooperation and integration in the industrial and technological field will be slow, and frequently painful, the risk of disillusionment is very great, and such disillusionment seems likely only to delay the process still further, or even to halt it altogether. A useful procedure might therefore be the redefinition of the problem in a form more amenable to solution. It may be objected that this makes any solution necessarily less ambitious, but the reply to this is that, given the difficulties in the technological field, better the high chance of a small success capable of steady expansion than the very low chance of a more dramatic breakthrough.

Two developments are necessary for a redefinition of the problem in the sense meant here. First, a more relaxed style is called for on the part of the Commission, worrying at concrete obstacles, following up half-initiatives made by governments, companies or other organisations, but not taking on itself, or seeking to take on, administrative responsibilities where the political ground is unsure. Second, a conscious assessment by governments, government by government and case by case, of the direct and indirect benefits of collaboration over a longer time scale than that within which they normally operate, coupled with some additional premium, its magnitude to be decided politically in each case, in favour of European-level action. There is no requirement that governments abdicate from defence of the national interest, nor need there be less intergovernmental argument in Europe. On the contrary, technological and industrial integration, if it is to come about, needs more argument, not less. Action on big issues needs must be preceded by argument on big issues, and it is argument not exhortation that Europe has lacked. Only weak negotiators will fear hard bargaining, but obviously there can be no hard bargaining if there is no bargaining at all. Only if governments and officials, companies and other organisations talk still more than they have done even in the last decade, and still make no greater progress, should one conclude that technological collaboration and cooperation have been overwritten. But, to repeat, while the EEC Commission can promote such confrontations, and support them with cogent factual analyses, it can hardly lead. The Commission already of course performs a considerable amount of what might be called European-level staff work in the technological field, but there is, one feels, a great deal more to be done in this direction without ending up on the farther shores of technological forecasting or futurology. It is freely conceded that 'Neither a purely European technology nor a purely European defence system, . . . would have any chance of catching up the vast distances that now separate them from American technology and American military capacity'.[18] This point is not really at issue. Even had Europe started politically united and technically level with the United States post-war, the realities of geography alone must eventually have created a major differential in the questions asked of their respective defence technologies. The immediate objectives of collaboration and cooperation, integration wholly apart, are instead rather to prevent new weaknesses developing, and to capitalise on Europe's many existing and potential strengths.

It is not easy, so far at least as technology is concerned, to have much confidence in any crisis theory of accelerated integration. On the civil side the technology-gap issue itself has so far manifestly failed to do much more than alert the interest of certain European elites, and to take an even more striking example from the field of military technology, Europe has been, and has had to be, content simply to provide a venue for the SALT talks. The initial outcome of these talks, the limitation on antiballistic missile deployment, benefits both the British and the French nuclear deterrents, in that it helps to maintain their credibility, and future outcomes may also be to Europe's advantage. But this initial benefit was largely accidental and, due allowance being made for consultation by the United States with her European allies, so also may future outcomes be. Paradoxically, in spite of all that has been said about the 'American challenge' in civil technology, so long as the United States retains a major defence interest in Western Europe, then the European nations can continue to put off the evolution of a truly European defence technology. Yet, while the crisis which would result from a real American withdrawal might be the only crisis serious enough greatly to accelerate integration of European defence technology and policy, it would surely be folly, strategically, politically and economically to wish for such a development.

Whatever the circumstances which eventually ensue, the assumption must not be made that European collaboration is the inevitable wave of the future. It probably will be, but it may also turn out to be a curious phenomenon of the sixties and seventies, a cul-de-sac blocked by entrenched national positions. What is quite certain is that if technology is to be one of the bricks from which a united Europe comes to be built, then this must be reflected in the way collaboration is fashioned, conducted and assessed. And even if the European nations stop far short of true economic and political integration, it is likely that they will find in collaboration that is pursued with wisdom an invaluable instrument for improving the material circumstances of their citizens, and, if appropriate projects are included, even perhaps of mankind more generally.

Notes

CHAPTER I

1. Even in 1965 *Flight* was surprised to discover how much collaboration there already was in the aerospace sector. 10 June 1965, pp. 908–40.

2. Miller, Linda B., 'Europe's Futures – Change and Continuity' 9 *Journal of Common Market Studies*, pp. 93–113 at p. 108. See also Watson, Alan, *Europe At Risk* (London: Harrap, 1972), p. 98.

3. But see The Select Committee on Science and Technology, Session 1971–72, First Report, 'Research and Development,' HC 237, and Fourth Report, 'Research and Development Policy', HC 308, together with the Government's replies, Cmnd. 5176 and Cmnd. 5177.

4. Vig, Norman J., *Science and Technology in British Politics* (London: Pergammon Press, 1968).

5. *See* Clarke, Sir Richard, *New Trends in Government* (London: HMSO, 1971), Civil Service College Studies, No. 1.

6. For two very different views see Broadway, Frank, *State Intervention in British Industry* 1964–68 (London: Kaye and Ward, 1969) and Moonman, Eric, *Reluctant Partnership* (London: Victor Gollancz, 1971). But see also Bray, Jeremy, *Decision in Government* (London: Victor Gollancz, 1970).

7. See Graham, Andrew, 'Industrial Policy', in Beckerman, Wilfred, ed., *The Labour Government's Economic Record* 1964–70 (London: Duckworth, 1972), pp. 178–217.

8. 'Business Brief', 24 October 1970, pp. 60–61.

9. Among the more useful of the contemporary short articles etc. on these changes are the following:—
Plowden, William, 'Mintech Moves On', *New Society*, 12 January 1967, pp. 51–53; Clarke, Sir Richard, 'The Structure of Mintech', *New Technology*, No. 14, February 1968; *The Ministry of Technology 1964–69*, published by the Ministry in 1969; Clarke, Sir Richard, 'The Shape of the New Mintech', *Financial Times*, 17 November 1969 and 'Mintech in Retrospect', *1 Omega*, 1973, pp. 25–38, 137–63; Part, Sir Anthony, 'The

Running of the DTI', *Financial Times*, 25 June 1971.

10. *Observer*, editorial, 27 November 1966, and Plowden, op. cit.

11. Quoted by Timothy Johnson and Nicholas Faith, *Sunday Times*, 21 June 1970.

12. See Young, Stephen, 'Reshaping Industry: The IRC in Retrospect', *New Society*, 19 November 1970 and McClelland, W. G., 'The IRC 1966–71: An Experimental Prod', *Three Banks Review*, No. 94, June 1972, pp. 32–42. Finally, see Beesley, M. E. and White, G. M., 'The Industrial Reorganisation Corporation: A Study in Choice of Public Management', **51**, *Public Administration*, Spring 1973, pp. 61–89.

13. **810** HC Debs. cols. 352–3, 357, 447 and 455. See also **811** HC Debs. col. 361, (WA).

14. **842** HC Debs. col. 251.

15. *The Times*, 16 and 22 June 1972.

16. Industry Bill as amended by Standing Committee H, Bill 178, and **841** HC Debs. cols. 2433 and 2436; **842** HC Debs. col. 264.

17. **837** HC Debs. cols. 1023–9.

18. **837** HC Debs. cols. 1126–30 and Standing Committee H, 12th Sitting, 11 July 1972, col. 561.

19. **842** HC Debs. cols 257–8; **837** HC Debs. col. 1022.

20. *New Technology*, No. 13, January 1968; *Sunday Times*, 22 January 1967 (of the IRC) and *The Times*, 10 October 1969 and 24 March 1968.

21. See, for instance, Nicholas Faith, *Sunday Times*, 8 March 1970; Press reports, 9 October 1970; See also **805** HC Debs. cols. 1212–15.

22. **312** HL Debs. col. 1202 (the Lord Chancellor).

23. Cf., say, *Guardian*, 22 March 1966 and *Economist*, 19 March 1966, with *Sunday Times*, 5 March 1972 and *Observer*, 27 February 1972.

24. *The Times*, editorial, 13 October 1971.

25. **837** HC Debs. cols. 1009–11 and 1020; **841** HC Debs. col. 2430.

26. *The Times*, 18 May 1972 and *Observer*, 21 May 1972.

27. *Financial Times*, 25 May 1972. See also his *Government and Market Economy* (London: Institute of Economic Affairs, 1971).

28. *Guardian*, 17 February 1967.

29. 'The Bloomers Britain Made', Roger Elgin, *Observer*, 5

January 1969, is typical.

30. Jewkes, John, *Government and High Technology* (London: The Institute of Economic Affairs, 1972), Occasional Paper 37.

31. Of the 'space industry' there is in this context little to say. British companies have been members of European satellite consortia (BAC, Hawker-Siddeley, GEC-Marconi, Elliot-Automation), have built or are building British civil and military satellites, for launch both with American rockets and with the British Black Arrow, and BAC have been a main subcontractor in the Intelsat communications satellite programme. On the launch vehicles side, apart from Hawker-Siddeley's manufacture of Blue Streak for the ELDO programme, both BAC and Bristol Aerojet have constructed sounding rockets, and Westland followed their successful Black Knight research rocket by becoming principal contractor for the Black Arrow. The cancellation of the latter was announced by the Government in 1971.

32. The Select Committee on Science and Technology, 'UK Computer Industry', vol. 1, Minutes of Evidence, HC 137 of 1969–70, pp. 357–63. See also Cmnd. 3660, and **761** HC Debs. cols. 607–9.

33. Keegan, Victor, 'Industry and Technology', in McKie, D. and Cook, C., *The Decade of Disillusion* (London: Macmillan, 1972).

34. Fourth Report from the Select Committee on Science and Technology, 'The Prospects for the United Kingdom Computer Industry in the 1970s', HC 621 of 1970–71, especially Qs 603–7, 615, 617 and 676; **812** HC Debs. cols. 419–20 (WA); **822** HC Debs. cols. 196–7 (WA); **840** HC Debs. cols. 34–40; **842** HC Debs. cols. 155–7 (WA); *The Times*, 7 January and 4 July 1972; *Financial Times*, 2 March 1971.

35. **768** HC Debs. cols. 1428–38. It was announced on 22 March 1973 that the nuclear industry was to be reorganised, leaving only one construction company.

CHAPTER II

1. *The Times*, 15 November 1966 and 14 November 1967.

2. Wilson, Harold, *The Labour Government* 1964–70, (London: Weidenfeld & Nicolson and Michael Joseph, 1971), p. 300 and *The*

Times, 15 November 1967.

3. *The United Kingdom and the European Communities*, Foreign Secretary's Statement, 4 July 1967, Cmnd. 3345, para. 8. See also *Britain and the European Communities: an Economic Assessment*, Cmnd. 4289, 1970, paras. 70–75 (high technology industries).

4. (London: Hamish Hamilton), pp. xiii, 3 and 32.

5. Spannier, David, ' "Le Défi Américain" and the British Response', *Banker*, v, 118, January 1968, pp. 23–7.

6. Quinn, J. B., 'Technological Competition: Europe vs U.S.', *44 Harvard Business Review*, 4, July–August 1966, pp. 113–30.

7. Richardson, Jacques, and Park, Ford, 'Why Europe Lags Behind', *Science and Technology*, May 1968, pp. 20–29. The authors stated that their five functional categories were based on the work of Theodore Suranyi-Unger of Stanford Research Institute. See also the latter's 'What is the Technology Gap?' 2 *Interplay*, 1, June–July 1968, pp. 22–5.

8. *Op. cit.*, pp. 8–11.

9. Dunning, John H., *The Role of American Investment in the British Economy*, PEP Broadsheet 507. See also *United States Industry in Britain*, Economists' Advisory Group, for *Financial Times*, London, 1973.

10. 'Business Brief', 17 December 1966.

11. Abs, Hermann Josef, *The United States and Europe, Competitors or Partners?* (Paris: Institut International d'Études Bancaires, 1969), p. 7.

12. But see the views of M. D. Steuer, reported in the *Sunday Times*, 2 November 1969.

13. *The Research and Development Effort* (Paris: OECD, 1965), pp. 36 and 53. See also the *Gaps in Technology between Member Countries* Series (Paris: OECD, 1968–70), General Report, six Sector Reports and Analytical Report.

14. Williams, B. R., 'Investment and Technology in Growth', *32 The Manchester School*, 1, January 1964, pp. 59–78. On the 'technological BOP' see *New Scientist*, 6 May 1971, pp. 326–7.

15. McLachlan, D. L. and Swann, D., *Competition Policy in the European Community* (London: Oxford U.P., 1967), p. 233.

16. McNamara, Robert, 'A Technological Gap or a Management Gap?', *NATO Newsletter*, April 1967, pp. 24–5.

17. Diebold, John, 'Is the Gap Technological?', *46 Foreign*

Affairs, 1967–8, pp. 276–91; *The Times*, 2 October 1967.

18. Ben-David, Joseph, *Fundamental Research and the Universities* (Paris: OECD, 1968), p. 22.

19. Levitt, Theodore, 'The Gap is Not Technological', *Public Interest*, No. 12, Summer 1968, pp. 119–24.

20. Pfaltzgraff, Robert L., *The Atlantic Community* (London: Van Nostrand, 1969), Chapter III, 'The Technology Gap', p. 77.

21. 15 October 1967. See also for example, Adams, Walter, ed., *The Brain Drain* (London: Collier-Macmillan Ltd., 1968); Cmnd. 3417, *The Brain Drain*; Wilson, James A., 'The Emigration of British Scientists', 5 *Minerva* 1, Autumn 1966, pp. 20–9 and *1 Minerva* (Documents), 3, Spring 1963, pp. 342–80.

22. **151** *Science*, 25 February 1966, pp. 976–8.

23. *International Herald Tribune*, 29 June 1967.

24. 3 December 1966, p. 1060 and 16 March 1968, pp. 71–6. See also 21 January 1967, pp. 197–8 and 18 November 1967, pp. 769–70.

25. *Opera Mundi*, 30 May 1968.

26. Quoted in Macioti, Manfredo, *Europe and Technology*, CPC Summer School Studies, CPC No. 390 (London: CPC, 1968), p. 5. Also see *New York Times*, 8 January 1968.

27. Gilpin, Robert, 'European Disunion and the Technology Gap', *Public Interest*, No. 10, Winter 1968, pp. 43–54, at p. 50. Not that even the larger European countries have been unconcerned about their industrial and technological primacy within Europe, see Behrman, Jack N., *National Interests and the Multinational Enterprise* (Englewood Cliffs, N. Jersey: Prentice-Hall, 1970), esp. pp. 161–72.

28. Gilpin, Robert, *France in the Age of the Scientific State* (Princeton, N. Jersey: Princeton U.P., 1968), pp. 451–2 and 456–9.

29. Spence, Daniel Lloyd, *Technology Gap in Perspective* (New York: Spartan Books, 1970), pp. 54 and 63.

30. See, for example, the *Sunday Telegraph*, 12 June 1966, the *Observer*, 20 November 1966 and the *Guardian*, 17 November 1966.

31. 'Scientific and Technological Aspects of the Extension of the European Communities', Doc 2279, Strasbourg, 1967, p. 30.

32. *Opinion on the Applications for Membership received from the United Kingdom, Ireland, Denmark and Norway*, Commission of the EEC, 1967, Brussels. Ch. 7, para. 147. See also Vellas, Pierre, *L'Europe Face à la Révolution Technologique Américaine* (Paris:

Dunod, 1969), p. 188.

33. Quoted by Leslie, S. C., 'Technological Unity in Europe: Massive Political Barriers', *Round Table*, 1968, pp. 154–68 at p. 160. See also Knapp, John, 'Would Britain profit from the EEC?', *Round Table*, 1967, pp. 166–76.

34. *The Times*, 19 September 1969, 6 and 14 January 1970; IRC, 1st Annual Report and Accounts, 1968, HC 252, para. 8; *Financial Times*, 19 September 1969, and comments of Mr Ronald Grierson, 7 March 1968.

35. McClelland, W. G., *op. cit.*

36. (London: Allen and Unwin, 1969). See also his articles in *The Times*, 17 August 1970 and 13 April 1967, and in the *Guardian*, 21 October 1966, and 'The Benefits of Scale for Industry' in Pinder, John, ed., *The Economics of Europe* (London: Charles Knight & Co., 1971), p. 48.

37. Mayne, Richard, ed., (London: Fontana-Collins for RIIA-PEP), chapter 11. And cf. Spinelli, Altiero, *The European Adventure* (London: Charles Knight & Co., 1972), chapter 8.

38. See Layton's 'A European Industrial Marriage Bureau', in *Industry and the Common Market* (London: Federal Trust for Education and Research, 1971), (Report of Conference, 7–8 October 1970), pp. 79–88 at p. 85.

39. *Problems of British Entry into the EEC: Reports to the Action Committee for the United States of Europe* (London: RIIA- PEP, 1969), European Series No. 11, pp. 68–95.

40. See for example 'European Cooperation in Advanced Technology', report of a conference arranged by the Movement, July 1965. Also in this context see conference reports on 'Industrial Integration in Europe' and 'European Technological Collaboration' (London: Federal Trust for Education and Research, 1968 and 1969). Still other conferences on the same basic theme were those on Transatlantic Technological Imbalance and Collaboration, Deauville, 25–28 May 1967, and the Pugwash Symposia at Marianske Lazne, 13–18 May 1968, Nice, 8–10 September 1968, and Noordwijk, 5–8 June 1970.

41. Foche, René, 'Europe and Technology', *Atlantic Papers*, 2 (Paris: The Atlantic Institute, 1970). Also note Knoppers, Antonie Theodoor, 'The Role of Science and Technology in Atlantic Economic Relationships', The Atlantic Institute, 1967.

42. Calmann, John, *Defence, Technology and the Western Alliance* (London: The Institute for Strategic Studies, 1967), No. 1.

43. Meyer, Sir Anthony, *A European Technological Community*, CPC, No. 357, (London: CPC, 1966).

44. See *The Times*, 9 June 1967.

45. Moonman, Eric, ed., *Science and Technology in Europe* (Harmondsworth: Penguin Books Ltd., 1968), p. 161. See also 'Report on Science and Technology in Europe', Parliamentary Labour Party Science and Technology Group, 1968 and *The Times*, 9 June 1967.

46. Reed, Laurance, *Europe in a Shrinking World* (London: Oldbourne, 1967), p. 183. See also his 'Ocean-Space – Europe's New Frontier', for the Bow Group, 1969.

47. Beck, Robert H., *et al.*, *The Changing Structure of Europe* (Minneapolis: The University Press, 1970), p. 237 and chapter 4, esp. pp. 96–104.

48. Basiuk, Victor, 'Technology, Western Europe's Alternative Futures, and American Policy', **15** *Orbis*, 2, Summer 1971, pp. 485–506.

49. Nau, Henry R., 'A Political Interpretation of the Technology Gap Dispute', **15** *Orbis*, 2, Summer 1971, pp. 507–27.

50. Schaerf, T. F., 'The Technological Gap: Issues, Policies and Trade Offs', **12** *Orbis*, 3, Fall 1968, pp. 852–72.

51. See **767** HC Debs. cols. 18–19.

52. *Convention on the Establishment of the International Institute for the Management of Technology*, Cmnd. 4854; **167** *Science*, 6 February 1970, pp. 850–2; Cade, J. A., 'The International Institute for the Management of Technology', *OECD Observer*, August 1970, pp. 44–9.

53. *Financial Times*, 14 December 1971; *Guardian*, 27 March 1972.

54. Wilshere, David, *Some Economic and Organisational Aspects of European Research and Development Effectiveness* (Berne: Herbert Lang and Co., 1970).

55. *Electronics International*, 8 May 1972, pp. 65 ff.; *Christian Science Monitor*, 29 December 1971 (Dr Harvey Brooks); Lessing, Lawrence, *Fortune*, April 1972, p. 69 ff.; See also Boffey, Philip, 'Technology and World Trade: Is there cause for alarm?', *Science*, 2 April 1971, pp. 37–41. Also Rhodes, J. B., 'The American

Challenge Challenged', *Harvard Business Review*, September–October 1969, p. 45 f.

56. Pavitt, Keith, 'Technology, International Competition, and Economic Growth: Some Lessons and Perspectives', 25 *World Politics*, 2, January 1973, pp. 183–205, concludes at pp. 190 and 201 that 'Europe appears to have responded very effectively to the "American challenge" . . . Individual European countries have been able to do very well on their own in science and technology . . . the USA has been losing its preponderance in the Western World's science and technology'.

57. Faith, Nicholas, *The Infiltrators* (London: Hamish Hamilton, 1971). See review by Mr Wedgwood Benn, *Sunday Times*, 7 November 1971.

58. *Sunday Times*, 3 December 1972. But cf. the *Daily Telegraph*, 20 February 1969 (W. Farr).

59. The literature on the multinational company is now virtually a field of its own and it seems best simply to list the works by which the present author has knowingly been influenced:—

Miles, Caroline, M., 'The International Corporation', 45 *International Affairs*, 1969, pp. 259–68; Turner, Louis, *Invisible Empires* (London: Hamish Hamilton, 1970); Tugendhat, Christopher, *The Multinationals* (London: Eyre and Spottiswoode, 1971); also various articles by Tugendhat in the *Financial Times*, e.g. 26 June and 12 August 1968, 5 September and 17 October 1969, 9 February 1970 and 2 December 1971; Vernon, Raymond, *Sovereignty at Bay* (London: Longman, 1971); Dunning, John H., ed., *The Multinational Enterprise*, (London: Allen and Unwin Ltd., 1971); Behrman, Jack N., *National Interests and the Multinational Enterprise, op. cit.*; Stephenson, Hugh, *The Coming Clash* (London: Weidenfeld and Nicolson, 1972); Kindleberger, Charles P., ed., *The International Corporation* (Cambridge, Mass.: The MIT Press, 1970), especially chapter 6 (Dunning, John H.), and chapter 8 (Waltz, Kenneth N.); Brooke, Michael Z. and Remmers, H. Lee, *The Strategy of Multinational Enterprise* (London: Longman, 1970) and *The Multinational Company in Europe* (London: Longman, 1972); Düren, Albrecht, 'Multinational Companies as a Political Problem', *World Today*, November 1972, pp. 473–82; Berschin, H. Herbert, 'Enterprises multinationales et intégration euro-

péenne', *Les Problèmes de l'Europe*, 53, Paris, 1971, pp. 31–7.
60. *Op. cit.*, p. 235.
61. *Op. cit.*, esp. pp. 2, 12 and 38–9.
62. Warner, Malcolm, 'Towards Transnational Trade Unions ?', *New Society*, 15 October 1970; *The Times*, 10 February 1973; *Sunday Times*, 9 April 1972; *Financial Times*, 27 July 1971.

CHAPTER III

1. Scheinman, Lawrence, 'Euratom: Nuclear Integration in Europe', *International Conciliation*, May 1967, No. 563, esp. pp. 8–9.
2. Polach, Jaroslav G., *Euratom: Its Background, Issues and Economic Implications* (Dobbs Ferry, N.Y.: Oceana Publications Inc., 1964), pp. 61 and 115.
3. Nieburg, H. L., 'Euratom: A Study in Coalition Politics', *15 World Politics*, 1962–3, pp. 597–622 at p. 597.
4. See, for instance, Gueron, J., 'The lessons to be learned from Euratom', *23 Bulletin of the Atomic Scientists*, March 1967, pp. 38–41. Also *Euronuclear*, February 1966, p. 83.
5. 'Survey of the Nuclear Policy of the European Community', *7 Euratom Quarterly Review*, 1968 (special issue), p. 130.
6. *158 Science*, 13 October 1967, p. 242–4.
7. Quoted in *European Community*, March 1969, p. 5.
8. Van Dijck, J. M., 'Euratom's Martyrdom', *9 Common Market*, 2, February 1969, pp. 42–44.
9. See *The Times*, 7 February 1973 and letter 29 January 1973; *European Community*, March 1973, p. 7. (Anthony Winning). An agreement on nuclear safeguards was signed between the EEC and the IAEA in April 1973.
10. See for instance Kraijenhoff, G., Conference on Industry and Society in the European Community, Venice, April 1972, paper 9, p. 32.
11. *Memorandum sur les Problèmes que pose le progrès scientifique et technique dans la communauté Européene* (Brussels: 20 March, 1967, EUR/C/1711/2/67f.); See also the French Note printed in Caty, Gilbert, *L'Europe Technologique* (Paris: Librairie Armand Colin, 1969). See also European Parliament Working Documents 1966–67, 23 September 1966, Doc 97, Report on 'Technological

Progress and Scientific Research in the European Community.'

12. *European Community*, December 1967, p. 3 and the *Financial Times*, 9 November 1967.

13. See Bourgiugnon, Pierre (Head of Planning and Implementation Section of the Research Division, EEC) in Into Europe, Conference organised by the London Chamber of Commerce, 2–4 February 1971, pp. 70–76.

14. See Commission des Communautes Européennes, 'Poursuite des travaux en matière de cooperation technologique' (Strasbourg: 15 May 1968, Sec. (68) 1524 final), European Parliament Working Documents 1968–9, 25 September 1968, Doc. 112, Report on 'The European Policy for Research and Technology', and *European Community*, December 1968, p. 4, October 1968, p. 2 and November 1968, p. 2.

15. European Communities Medium Term Economic Policy Committee, 'Scientific and Technical Cooperation between European Countries: Possibilities in Seven Sectors'. Report of the Working Party on 'Scientific and Technical Research Policy' (Brussels: 9 April 1969, 7301/II/69-E). Also 'Additional Documents' (10.121/II/69-E), Doc R/1651/69 (RECH9) of 24 September 1969, and Doc R/1655/69 (RECH 10) of 30 September 1969. Also see SEC (70) 2083 final of 17 June 1970.

16. *Sunday Times*, 29 June 1969 and *The Times*, 27 June 1969.

17. Layton, Christopher, 'Wanted: a common strategy on technology', *European Community*, February 1970, pp. 16–17.

18. *Guardian*, 24 November 1971, quoting Mr Corfield, and *Le Monde*, 25 November 1971. Contributions by the EEC countries to international projects, as a percentage of their total research effort, had fallen from 13·7 per cent in 1967 to 11·4 in 1969, though in absolute terms were up by 18·2. Medium Term Economic Policy Committee, 'Public Financing of R & D in the Community Countries 1967–1970', Report by the Statistical Experts Group to the PREST Group, Nr 1 – September 1970, EUR 4532 d, f, e, p. 36.

19. 'Note de la Commission au Conseil concernant une action communautaire d'ensemble en matière de recherche et du developpement scientifique et technologique' (Brussels: 11 November 1970, SEC(70) 4250), and 'Objectifs et moyens pour une politique commune de la recherche scientifique et du developpement

technologique' (Brussels: 14 June 1972, COM (72) 700).

20. See also Foix, François, 'La Politique communautaire de la recherche et du developpement', Doctoral Thesis, University of Toulouse, December 1969; Commission des Communautes Euro-péenes, 'Les Cadres juridiques de la coopération internationale en matière scientifique et le problème Européen' (Brussels: 31 May 1970, Report of the Aix en Provence and Nice Conferences); 'La Politique scientifique en Europe' (Dossier Bibliographique), Communautes Européennes, 1967.

21. Commission memorandum to the Council on the establish-ment of European companies, Supplement to *Bulletin of the EEC*, No. 9/10, 1966.

22. Guido Colonna di Paliano, in a paper to the British Council for the European Movement, London, 6 June 1968, reported in *European Community*, July–August 1968, pp. 4–5.

23. Commission des Communautes Européennes, 'La Politique industrielle de la communauté', Memorandum de la Commission au Conseil (Brussels, 18 March 1970), COM (70) 100 final; 'Pro-posed Statute for the European Company', supplement to *Bulletin of the European Communities*, No. 8, 1970.

24. Thompson, Dennis, *The Proposal for a European Company* (London: RIIA-PEP, 1969), European Series, No. 13; 'Company Law and the EEC', *Financial Times*, 28 June 1972; also articles by Professor Clive Schmitthoff, *The Times*, 29 December 1972, and 1 January 1973.

25. Mann, F. A., 'The European Company', *International and Comparative Law Quarterly*, vol. 19, pt. 3, July 1970, pp. 468–82.

26. Düren, Albrecht, 'Multinational Companies as a Political Problem', *World Today*, November 1972, pp. 473–82, at p. 475.

27. Vasseur, Michel, 'Towards a European Company: 1', *Round Table*, No. 248, October 1972, pp. 519–27.

28. *Financial Times*, 25 September 1970, *Observer*, 26 May 1968, and *The Times*, 30 September 1970. See also Siekman, Philip, 'Europe's Love Affair with Bigness', *Fortune*, March 1970, pp. 95f. The Dunlop-Pirelli union was 'shaken to its foundations' in early 1973 as a result of a loss by the Italian subsidiary of some £38·6 millions in the two years following the link between the companies. However this crisis was much more a matter of ordinary, if un-successful, business than a merger problem. See, for instance, the

Observer, 21 January 1973, and *The Times*, 26 January 1973.

29. This is actually quoted from Layton, Christopher, *Cross Frontier Mergers in Europe* (Bath: Bath University Press, 1971), but the point had been taken by the Commission considerably before this.

30. *European Community*, May 1971, p. 8, December 1971, p. 6, and January 1972, p. 8.

31. *The Times*, 2 June 1972.

32. Note West German queries about Britain's 1972 Industry Bill, e.g. *The Times*, 9 August 1972.

33. Silver, C. L., 'Problems set Candidate Countries by the EEC Technological Policy', *Revue du Marché Commun*, No. 153, April 1972, pp. 321–7 (Nice Conference, 10–11 December 1971) Mr Silver is an assistant secretary at the DTI.

34. 'Industrial Policy: Status Report on the Community's Work', (Report by R. Toulemon to the Industry and Society in the European Community Conference, Venice, 20–22 April, 1972), *Bulletin of the European Communities*, vol. 5, No. 6, 1972, pp. 13–36 at p. 28. (Note also Procs. No. VIII, *Objectives and Resources for a European Technological Development Policy*).

35. *European Community*, November 1972, p. 25.

36. Quoted from 'Objectives and Instruments of a Common Policy for Scientific Research and Technological Development' *Bulletin of the European Communities*, Supplement 6, 1972. The first meeting of CERD took place on 4 April 1973, under the chairmanship of Professor H. Casimir.

37. Cf. **239**, *Nature*, 6 October 1972, editorial: 'it will be best if European technology can be coordinated not from Brussels but by the evolution of institutions in which existing research organisations, the manufacturers with whom they work and the potential customers are intimately related.' Also *243*, 18 May 1973.

38. E.g.: 'the UK and other would-be members . . . would make industrial policy one of the development fields *par excellence* of the enlarged Community', H. E. Guido Colonna di Paliano, *Bulletin of the European Communities*, No. 5, 1970, pp. 7–9.

39. *Engineer*, interview with Mr C. Chataway, 24–31 August 1971, pp. 30–31.

40. *The Times*, 3 and 20 October 1972 and *Sunday Times*, 22 October 1972.

41. For general background, see the Second Industrial Appraisal on Britain in Europe, conducted by the CBI, London, 1970.

42. *New Scientist*, 15 March 1973, p. 587, reported an 'unholy alliance' between Britain and France at Brussels regarding a Community technology policy; Britain arguing for an *à la carte*, sectoral approach. See also *ibid.*, 12 April 1973, pp. 105–7.

CHAPTER IV

1. **822** HC Debs. cols 15–16, (WA).

2. *Le Monde*, 6 May 1966, quoted in Gilpin, *op. cit.*, *France in the Age of the Scientific State*. Cf. Derek Ezra, writing in *The Times*, 2 January 1973.

3. Simpson, John and Gregory, Frank, 'West European Collaboration in Weapons Procurement', **16** *Orbis*, 2, Summer 1972, pp. 435–61.

4. On Concorde generally see:—
Davis, John, *The Concorde Affair*, (London: Frewin, 1969); Wiggs, Richard, *Concorde* (London: Pan, 1971); Costello, John and Hughes, Terry, *The Battle for Concorde* (Salisbury: Compton Press, 1971); Blackall, T. E., *Concorde* (Henley: Foulis, 1969); Faculté de Droit et des Sciences Economiques de l'Université de Nice, *La Coopération internationale*, 1, June 1970, pp. 37–44 (bibliography). Reed, Arthur, *Britain's Aircraft Industry: What Went Right? What Went Wrong?* (London: Dent, 1973) was published too late to be of use for the present study.

5. **817** HC Debs. cols 10–12; **774** HC Debs. col 478; **803** HC Debs. cols 300 and 1118.

6. Franks. P. R., 'The Management Organisation of the Martel Project', *Aeronautical Journal*, January 1970, pp. 81–4; Gee, Jack, *Mirage* (London: Macdonald, 1971) pp. 87–97 and 173–7.

7. *The Times*, 17 January 1967; **739** HC Debs. cols 405–8; **742** HC Debs. cols 477–80; **744** HC Debs. col 185 (WA), **745** HC Debs. col 149 (WA).

8. **743** HC Debs. cols 1678–80; **749** HC Debs. cols 1825 and 1832; *Aviation Week*, 3 May 1971, p. 45; *Flight*, 29 June 1967, p. 1037; *Guardian*, 8 November and 12 December 1966.

9. E.g. **329** HL Debs. col 457.

10. Layton, Christopher, Harlow, Christopher, and de Hoghton,

Charles, *Ten Innovations* (London: Allen & Unwin for PEP, 1972), chapter 3 'Variable Geometry Aircraft'.

11. James, Robert Rhodes, 'Standardisation and Common Production of Weapons in Nato', *Defence, Technology and the Western Alliance*, No. 3, (London: Institute for Strategic Studies, 1967), p. 11.

12. Edmonds, Martin, 'International Collaboration in Weapons Procurement', *43 International Affairs*, 2, April 1967, pp. 252–64.

13. 735 HC Debs. col 1025.

14. *Report of the Committee of Inquiry into the Aircraft Industry*, 1965, Cmnd 2853, para. 272.

15. Heath, B. O., 'The MRCA Project', *Aeronautical Journal*, June 1970, pp. 444–55.

16. Second Report from the Expenditure Committee, HC 141 of 1971–2, report para. 38.

17. 713 HC Debs. col 1696.

18. Cmnd 2902, p. 45. Cf. Cmnd. 3345, para. 8.

19. *Flight*, 29 October 1970, p. 680.

20. Third Report from the Committee of Public Accounts, HC 447 of 1971–2, report paras 27–35, and Qs. 1096A, 1097A, 1129.

21. See, for instance, 751 HC Debs. cols 419–20; 767 HC Debs. cols 1–4; 781 HC Debs. cols 1125–8; 807 HC Debs. cols 1286–94; *Observer*, 27 August 1967; *Guardian*, 17 February 1967; *New Scientist*, 12 November 1970, p. 334; *Flight*, 11 August, 1967. Also cf. *The Times* 23 and 27 October 1970.

22. *Flight*, 3 June 1965, p. 869 (interview with Mr Roy Jenkins, Minister of Aviation). Also see 27 May 1965, p. 814.

23. *The Times*, 8 August 1972.

24. See 767 HC Debs. cols 107–8, and 807 HC Debs. col 475, (WAs).

25. *Op. cit.*, Cmnd. 2853, paras 260–2.

26. 'Productivity of the National Aircraft Effort', Report of a Committee appointed by the Minister of Technology and the President of the S.B.A.C., chairman Mr St. John Elstub, HMSO, 1969, (Conclusions). See also J. M. Ramsden, editor of *Flight*, *The Times*, 4 October 1971.

27. The Air League, *The United Kingdom Aerospace Industry*, (London: October 1971), p. 7. Cf. 'Military Aircraft Procurement

and its Effect on the British Aerospace Industry', RUSI Seminar, 23 October, 1968, Report p. 5 (Jeffrey Quill).

28. Mallaleiu, J. W. P., *New Scientist*, 8 May 1969, pp. 294–5.

29. See *The Times*, 19 October 1972.

30. See Roger Elgin, writing in the *Sunday Times*, 11 February 1973.

31. *Atom*, August 1969, p. 216.

32. 814 HC Debs. col 511 and 817 HC Debs. cols 10–12.

33. 811 HC Debs. col 820. For a comment on Roll's earlier attitude see *Flight*, 4 January 1973, p. 17.

34. *Jane's All the World's Aircraft* 1972–73 (London: Sampson Low, Marston & Co., Ltd., 1972), p. 677.

35. *Aviation Week*, 21 August 1972, p. 12, and 11 September 1972, p. 23; *Flight*, 30 November 1972, p. 764, 16 November 1972, p. 681 and 4 January 1973, editorial.

36. *The Times*, 4 October 1971.

37. E.g. 329 HL Debs. col 488; 846 HC Debs. col 25; 'Civil and Military Aviation Policy for Europe', Report of the Committee on Scientific, Technological and Aerospace questions of the Western European Union, 1972. Doc 592. See also *Flight*, 9 November 1972, p. 650 and 4 January 1973, pp. 17–18.

38. 828 HC Debs. col 641; 846 HC Debs. col 25; *Financial Times*, 4 September 1971 and *The Times*, 29 September 1972. *Flight*, 14 December 1972, p. 162.

39. *The Times*, 3 and 16 June 1971.

40. *The Times*, 5 October 1972.

41. Joucla, Gérard, *La Coopération Internationale dans les Industries Aéronautiques Européennes* (Paris: Librairie General de Droit et de Jurisprudence, 1971) pp. 130–34.

42. Commission of the European Communities, *The Aeronautical and Space Industries of the Community Compared with those of the United Kingdom and United States*, 'Competition Industry – 1971–4', Brussels 1971 (The SORIS report), vol. 4, pp. 976–8.

43. See *Flight*, 4 and 20 January 1973 (S. B. Saul).

44. Beteille, R., 'The Coordination of European Research', *Aeronautical Journal*, May 1969, pp. 417–20.

45. See also *Communication de la commission au conseil concernant les actions de politique industrielle et technologique de la Communauté à entreprendre dans le secteur aeronautique*, COM (72) 850, Brussels,

12 July 1972, p. 27. See also pp. 12–15.

46. A useful article is Pfaltzgraff, Robert L., Jr., and Deghand, James L., 'European Technological Collaboration: The Experience of the European Launcher Development Organisation. (ELDO),' 7 *Journal of Common Market Studies*, 1, pp. 22–34.

47. See also Western European Union Docs 388 (1966), 402 (1967) and 429 (1967).

48. Second Report from the Estimates Committee, 'The European Space Vehicle Launcher Development Organisation (ELDO)', HC 148 of 1966–7, Report, para. 20; and ELDO Report 1960–65 to the Council of Europe (Paris: 1965) p. 13.

49. Thirteenth Report from the Estimates Committee, 'Space Research and Development', HC 601 of 1966–7, p. 157.

50. Fifth Report from the Select Committee on Science and Technology, 'United Kingdom Space Activities', HC 629 of 1970–71, Q 595.

51. *Op. cit.*, HC 148 of 1966–7, Q 406, Report para. 36, and Appendix 2, p. 154.

52. **729** HC Debs. cols 1027–8; cf. *op. cit.*, HC 148 of 1966–7, Qs 431 and 594; **740** HC Debs. col 1448.

53. **763** HC Debs. cols 40–41; **779** HC Debs. col 395.

54. *Op. cit.*, HC 629 of 1970–71, Q 418.

55. *Ibid.*, Qs 364 and 1020.

56. *Ibid.*, Q 1036 and HC Debs., **808**, cols 381–6. See also *New Scientist*, 12 November 1970, p. 324, and Valentine, Burl, 'Obstacles to space cooperation: Europe and the post-Apollo experience', *1 Research Policy*, 2, pp. 104–21.

57. *Op. cit.*, HC 629, p. 330.

58. *Ibid.*, Q 1011 and **804** HC Debs. cols 457–69 and **803** HC Debs. col 1107.

59. NISC memo, at p. 219 and BAC memo, at p. 75.

60. See *Aviation Week*, 24 July 1972.

61. See *The Times*, 24 October 1972 and the *Sunday Times*, 22 October 1972.

62. Cairns, David, 'Bleak Future for Joint Space Effort', *European Community*, April 1972, pp. 19–20.

63. *Intervia*, 1972, No. 9, p. 921.

64. Mentioned for instance in *Flight*, 30 November 1972, p. 764.

65. *Interavia*, 1972, No. 12, pp. 1305–7.

66. *Op. cit.*, HC 629 of 1970–71, Report, para. 106, and **804** HC Debs. cols 457–69.

67. *Op. cit.*, HC 629 of 1970–71, p. 316, ESRO Secretariat memo., para. 1.

68. *Ibid.*, p. 32, Ministry of Aviation Supply memo., para. 7(2)iii.

69. See Council of Europe, Doc. 3064, 'Report on European Space Policy', 16 December 1971, paras 22–4. Cf. also the earlier report with this title, Doc. 2243, 1967.

70. *New Scientist*, 22 July 1971, p. 176.

71. *Ibid.*, 18 January 1973, pp. 129–30.

72. *Guardian*, 22 July 1969.

73. *Financial Times*, 20 May 1968, and **833** HC Debs. col 74 (WA); *Opera Mundi*, 27 June 1968.

74. *Financial Times*, 27 November 1969. (Mintech Spokesman).

75. 18 September 1971, p. 70.

76. E.g. *Nucleonics Week*, 25 September 1969; *New Scientist*, 19 October 1972, p. 132; also note West German opposition to GGA's operations – *The Times*, 20 October 1972.

77. Albonetti, Achille, *Europe and Nuclear Energy*, (Paris: Atlantic Institute, 1972) The Atlantic Papers, 2, 1972.

78. *Nucleonics Week*, 4 September 1969; *Nuclear Engineering*, August 1970, p. 579.

79. Epstein, Barbara, 'Politics of Trade in Power Plant', Trade Policy Research Centre, 1971, Conclusions.

80. Lord Sherfield, 'The Civil Applications of Nuclear Energy: Prospects for European Development,' *Round Table*, No. 246, April 1972, pp. 175–86.

81. *Nucleonics Week*, 1 August 1968 and the *Financial Times*, 2 October 1968.

82. Cf. *Nuclear Engineering*, November 1972, p. 895.

83. *Financial Times*, 12 May, 20 October, 11 and 23 December 1971 and 11 January 1972; *Nuclear Engineering*, June 1972, p. 432 and August 1972, pp. 580–1 and 583.

84. *Financial Times*, 6 July 1970 and 15 July 1972; *Nuclear Engineering*, August 1971, pp. 607 and 611; *New Scientist*, 10 December 1970, p. 435.

85. **775** HC Debs. cols 156–7 (WA); **781** HC Debs. cols 1140–1; **793** HC Debs. cols 1732–1740.

86. *Financial Times*, 23 and 29 October 1969, 13 October 1971

and 17 April 1970.

87. *Ibid.*, 22 December 1969, and, for example the *Observer*, 16 March 1969.

88. *New Scientist*, 15 February 1968 (J. A. Redeker); *Nuclear Engineering*, November 1970, p. 853; *Financial Times*, 1 March 1972.

89. Barnaby, C. F., 'The Gas Centrifuge Project', *Science Journal*, August 1969, pp. 54–9; *Observer*, 9 February 1969; *Opera Mundi*, 30 January 1969; *Nuclear Engineering*, March 1969, p. 160. *Financial Times*, 29 January and 13 February 1970.

90. McKnight, Allan, *Guardian*, 20 February 1969.

91. *The Times*, 23 January and 18 June 1969.

92. Owen, David, *The Politics of Defence* (London: Jonathan Cape, 1972), pp. 220–24.

93. Heath, Edward, *Old World, New Horizons: Britain, the Common Market and the Atlantic Alliance*, (London: Oxford U.P., 1970), p. 73. See also his 'Realism in British Foreign Policy', *48 Foreign Affairs*, 1, October 1969, pp. 39–50.

94. See *Le Monde*, 20 October 1971; 'Our Future in Europe: the Long Term Case for Going In', Bow Group, 1970: *Financial Times*, 31 July 1970.

95. See *The Times*, 14, 18 and 23 (editorial) October 1972.

96. Pierre, Andrew J., *Nuclear Politics* (London: Oxford U.P., 1972) pp. 335–9; see also Smart, Ian, *Future Conditional: the Prospect for Anglo-French Nuclear Cooperation* (London: Institute for Strategic Studies, 1971), Adelphi Paper 78; and Brenner, Michael J., 'Strategic Interdependence and the Politics of Inertia', *23 World Politics*, 4, July 1971, pp. 635–64. Lord Carrington told the RUSI in April 1973 that Britain was not 'actively engaged' in making any arrangements with France – *The Times*, 4 April 1973.

97. Debré, Michel, 'France's Global Strategy', *49 Foreign Affairs*, 3, April 1971, pp. 395–406 at p. 401; *The Times* 5 and 7 December 1972.

98. See, for instance, *The Times*, 6 February 1973 and *Sunday Times*, 4 February 1973.

99. *The Times*, 21 February 1973, report of an article by M. Debré in *Le Point*. M. Debré was not a member of the Government formed by M. Messmer in April 1973.

100. Thomson, George, 'The Politics of Anglo-French Nuclear Weapons', *Round Table*, No. 246, April 1972, pp. 157–63.

101. *Ibid.*, Barzel, Rainer, 'The Nuclear Defence of Western Europe', pp. 165–74.

102. Duchêne, François, writing in *The Times*, 26 February 1973; also in *Survival*, Jan.-Feb., 1973, pp. 2–7.

103. Fourth Report from the Select Committee on Science and Technology, 'The Prospects for the U.K. Computer Industry in the 1970's, HC 621 1970–71, (Evidence is 621 II and III of 1970–71, and HC 137 and 272 of 1969–70). HC 621 II of 1970–71, Q 369 and HC 621 III of 1970–71, Appendix 1; See also *The Times*, 7 October and 30 December 1971.

104. See Harman, Alvin J., *The International Computer Industry* (Cambridge, Mass.: Harvard U.P., 1971).

105. De la Mahotière, Stuart, *Towards One Europe*, (Harmondsworth: Pelican Books, 1970), chapter 4, 'The Technological Gap', at p. 93.

106. Council of Europe, Doc. 2893, 'Report on the Computer Industry in Europe: Hardware Manufacturing', Strasbourg, 1971, paras 60, 85 and 96–98; *Financial Times*, 12 August 1971 and 28 January 1972; *New Scientist*, 10 February 1972; HC 621 III 1970–71 *op. cit.*, Appendix 32.

107. *Op. cit.*, HC 621 II of 1970–71 Q 1693.

108. *Op. cit.*, Doc. 2893.

109. *Financial Times*, 28 June 1972.

110. *New Scientist*, 17 February 1970, p. 488; *op. cit.*, HC 621 I of 1970–71, Q 914 and report para. 127.

111. *Op. cit.*, HC 137 of 1969–70, Q 2016 (The Minister of Technology).

112. *Op. cit.*, HC 137 of 1969–70, Q 54.

113. *Ibid.*, ICL memo., paras 11 and 13.

114. *New Scientist*, 9 December 1971, p. 88, 21 May 1970, pp. 384–5 and 10 February 1972, p. 308; *The Times*, 2 February 1972.

115. *Ibid.*, 8 February 1973, and 27 May 1973.

116. *Ibid.*, 26 January 1973.

117. 24 April 1967; see also 3 May 1973.

118. 7 August 1972; see also 22 March 1973 and Cmnd. 5256.

CHAPTER V

1. *Science Policy and the European States*, Unesco Science

Policy Studies and Documents No. 25. (Paris: 1971) p. 179, para. 13.

2. *Government Organisation for Defence Procurement and Civil Aerospace*, Report of the Project Team led by Mr D. G. Rayner, Cmnd 4641, April 1971, para. 8, p. 18.

3. Kenrick, K. G., *The Advanced Industries of the 1970's and their European Development*, (London: Inbucon Group, 1969), p. 5.

4. White, C. B., 'Legal aspects of international cooperation on aircraft design and production: Cooperation between the parties to the project itself and third parties', *Aeronautical Journal*, March 1972, pp. 192–4.

5. Whitehead, Michael, 'The Economics of Technology in the Common Market', 7 *Technology and Society*, 3, pp. 88–90.

6. Layton, Christopher, *Cross Frontier Mergers in Europe*, (Bath: Bath University Press, 1971), pp. 9–10 and 20–23. Simpson and Gregory, *op. cit.*, distinguish in weapons procurement certain interesting subtypes which seem to fall in this category:

   (a) cases where a government insists on its national companies receiving specific subcontracts, as in the Belgian purchase of French Mirage aircraft.

   (b) cases where transnational groups produce for a single country, as in the production of the Kormoran anti-ship missile for West Germany by MBB and Aérospatiale, the Otomat anti-ship missile for Italy by Engins Matra and Oto Melara, and the PFZ-C anti-aircraft tank for the Netherlands by a West German, Swiss and Dutch consortium.

   (c) cases where the transnational venture is a private one, such as the Atlas missile (BAC and FN of Belgium) or the Vickers-Ingenieur Konton Lubeck diesel electric submarine.

7. White, *op. cit.*

8. SORIS report, vol. 2, p. 344.

9. *Flight*, 28 October 1971, pp. 685–9, 6 April 1972 (supplement). M. Ziegler is President of Aérospatiale.

10. *Ibid.*, 6 April 1972; *Sunday Times*, 9 April 1972; *Aviation Week*, 24 April 1972.

11. *Flight*, 7 October 1971, p. 560; *Aviation Week*, 24 April 1972, p. 39.

12. 1971, No. 2, p. 111. The author is grateful for assistance received from the CBI as regards the characteristics of the GIE.

13. Franks, *op. cit.*

14. Giusta, L., 'European Cooperation in the Aviation Industry and its Future Development. Instance of its Application to the Anglo-French Helicopter Programme', *Aeronautical Journal*, July 1969, pp. 573–80.

15. *Statement on the Defence Estimates* 1967, Cmnd 3203, p. 46.

16. **806** HC Debs. col 1209.

17. **811** HC Debs. col 578 (WA); *Flight*, 8 April 1971, pp. 484a–7.

18. Greenwood, A. H. C., 'Cooperation in Aerospace Projects', in *Industry and the Common Market* (London: Federal Trust for Education and Research, 1971), Report of Conference, 7–8 October 1970, pp. 4–15 at p. 12.

19. E.g. Mr Geoffrey Rippon, reported in *Aviation Week*, 11 September 1972, p. 21; see also *Financial Times*, 15 June 1971 and 10 September 1970.

20. *Financial Times*, 25 November 1971 (A. H. C. Greenwood of BAC).

21. *Flight*, 8 April 1971, p. 484.

22. Jenkins, W. B., 'Legal Aspects of International Cooperation on aircraft design and production: cooperation between the collaborating parties', *Aeronautical Journal*, March 1972, pp. 188–91.

23. Published in the *Aeronautical Journal*, May 1971, pp. 305–9.

24. *Op. cit.*, HC 629 of 1970–71, Qs 754 and 771–2.

25. Iserland, K., 'The Activities of ELDO', *Aeronautical Journal*, July 1968, pp. 574–83. and *op. cit.*, HC 148 of 1966–7, Q 936.

26. *Op. cit.*, HC 629 of 1970–71, Q 152.

27. Cf. Cmnd 2391 and Cmnd 2489, both 1964.

28. SORIS report, vol. 3, p. 523.

29. See CECLES-ELDO, Annual Report for 1967 to the Council of Europe, chapter I.

30. Nouille, J., 'The ELDO-PAS Programme and its Management', *Aeronautical Journal*, July 1968, pp. 584–7.

31. The conclusions of the report were summarised in *Flight*, 29 June 1972, pp. 965–6; see also *Interavia*, No. 9, 1972, p. 922.

32. *New Scientist*, 22 June 1972, p. 685.

33. *The Times*, 22 December 1972; *New Scientist*, 4 January

1973, p. 4.

34. *Nuclear Engineering*, March 1969, p. 159.

35. Greenhalgh, G. H., 7 *Journal of the British Nuclear Energy Society*, 3, July 1968, pp. 189–90; *The Times*, 15 May 1970.

36. Häfele, W., 'The German-Benelux fast breeder reactor project and future developments in European fast breeder reactors', *10 Journal of the BNES*, 1, January 1971, pp. 169–76, at pp. 172–3.

37. **783** HC Debs. col 1609, and **793** HC Debs. cols 1732–40; *Financial Times*, 4 August 1971; *Nucleonics Week*, 20 November 1969; *New Scientist*, 5 October 1972, pp. 12–16.

38. Ashcroft, Geoffrey, *Military Logistic Systems in NATO: the Goal of Integration. Pt. I: Economic Aspects* (London: The Institute for Strategic Studies, 1969), Adelphi Papers, No. 62, p. 20.

39. Third Report from the Committee of Public Accounts, HC 265 of 1964–5, C and AG's memo, para. 5, Qs 654–67; 5th Report from the Committee of Public Accounts, HC 647 of 1966–7 II, C and AG's memo, para. 7; **722** HC Debs. col 282.

40. *Op. cit.*, HC 265 of 1964–5, C and AG's memo, para. 6, Qs 660–1, 700, report para. 27.

41. Second Report from the Committee of Public Accounts, HC 158 of 1966–7, I, Q 778.

42. *Ibid.*, report, para. 28 and **737** HC Debs. col 96.

43. Second Report from the Estimates Committee, HC 42 of 1963–4, Qs 1182–3, 1398; *op. cit.*, HC 265 of 1964–5, Qs 624–30; *op. cit.*, HC 647 of 1966–7, Qs 1357–9, 1364, 1370, 1458–9, and C and AG's memo, para. 6.

44. Third Report from the Committee of Public Accounts, HC 362 of 1968–9, Qs 4799–4802 and *Flight*, 7 December 1967, p. 927.

45. Smith, A. H., 'The Development of the WE13', paper to Royal Aeronautical Society Motorcraft Section, 13 January 1972, (Westland Helicopters: 1972); **309** HL Debs. col 519; *Flight*, 10 February 1972, p. 236, 16 March 1972, p. 370 and 3 August 1972, pp. 166–7.

46. Evans, L. G., 'Joint Venture and International Collaboration', *Aeronautical Journal*, October 1971, pp. 752–9.

47. See *The Times*, 29 September 1971, (Kenneth Warren); *Sunday Times*, 5 September 1971, 3 October 1971 and 12 March 1972.

48. Greenwood, A. H. C., 'MRCA – The Future System of

Military Procurement', RUSI *Journal*, September 1972, pp. 3–13.

49. *Flight*, 24 June 1971 and *The Times*, 4 October 1971.

50. 16 May 1969.

51. **823** HC Debs. cols 885–6; **826** HC Debs. cols 181–2, (WA); *Aviation Week*, 24 April 1972; *Flight*, 4 May 1972; *Financial Times*, 22 January 1972; *op. cit.*, HC 141 of 1971–2, Q 1908.

52. **823** HC Debs. col 899.

53. *The Times*, 4 October 1971, (Michael J. Cobham, chairman of FLIGHT REFUELLING); see also the *Financial Times*, 7 August 1970.

54. Quoted in *Flight*, 2 July 1970, pp. 27–8.

55. Electronic Engineering Association, 'Formula for Success', London, March 1970, p. 6; also Annual Report 1971, p. 10.

56. *Interavia*, June 1971, p. 711 and September 1972, p. 957–8; *Flight*, 16 July 1970, p. 69 and 4 May 1972, p. 617.

57. Edwards, Sir George, *Partnership in Major Technological Projects*, 7th Maurice Lubbock Memorial Lecture (Oxford: Oxford U.P., 1970), pp. 28 and 42.

58. Society of British Aerospace Companies, 'A Future Plan for Britain's Aerospace Industry' (London: January 1972), paras. 19–23.

59. *Flight*, 16 December 1971, p. 976.

60. 28 October 1971 and 16 April 1970.

61. Joucla, *op. cit.*, pp. 100–20.

62. Report of the Steering Group on 'Development Cost Estimating', chairman W. E. Downey, HMSO, 1969, paras 207–9.

63. *Op. cit.*, HC 629 of 1970–71, Qs 1016–7; and see **329** HL Debs. col 480.

64. *Op. cit.*, HC 601 of 1966–7, Qs 1717, 1963–5; also pp. 272 and 346, and report paras 37 and 47.

65. *Op. cit.*, HC 148 of 1966–7, Qs 630–33, 733, 741, also p. 109 and report, para. 30; *op. cit.*, HC 601 of 1966–7, Q 966; and *op. cit.*, HC 629 of 1970–71, report, para. 67.

66. *Op. cit.*, HC 148 of 1966–7, report, para. 72, and 3rd Special Report from the Estimates Committee, HC 85 of 1967–8, p. 4 (departmental observations).

67. *Op. cit.*, HC 629 of 1970–71, Qs 147, 559, 853.

68. Crane, Diana, 'Transnational Networks in Basic Science', *25 International Organisation*, Summer 1971, pp. 588 and 593.

69. See, for example, *New Scientist*, 18 February 1971, pp. 350–2.

70. *The Times*, 2 June 1972.

71. Report to the Council of Europe, *A Preliminary Examination of Intergovernmental Cooperation in Science and Technology Affecting Western Europe*, (Project-Perseus) Science Policy Research Unit, University of Sussex, November 1971, Appendix B.

72. Despite Assembly of Western European Union, Doc. 522, 'Political Decision-Making and Advanced Technology', 7 October 1970, para. 57.

73. Burrows, Sir Bernard, and Irwin Christopher, *The Security of Western Europe*, (London: Charles Knight and Co., 1972), pp. 105–7.

74. *Op. cit.*, HC 629 of 1970–71, Q1009.

CHAPTER VI

1. Hill, Walter, *European Business*, No. 29, Spring 1971, pp. 61–72.

2. See for instance **801** HC Debs. col 22, (WA); **806** HC Debs. cols 1212–5; and **740** HC Debs. col 1059.

3. See the SORIS report, vol. 2, Section 3.4, pp. 328–44.

4. Second Report from the Select Committee on Science and Technology, 'Defence Research', HC 213 of 1968–9, Appendix 2.

5. Ziegler, H., *Collaboration Européenne dans la construction aéronautique*, AICMA Symposium, September 13–14 1967, and Edwards, Sir George, *Partnership in Major Technological Projects*, *op. cit.*, pp. 23–5.

6. Second Report from the Estimates Committee, 'Transport Aircraft', HC 42 of 1963–4, Qs 838–9, 1163, 1392–3 and 1395; and **669** HC Debs. cols 1638 and 1648.

7. Third Report from the Committee of Public Accounts, HC 265 of 1964–5, Qs 653 and 679, and C and AG's memo, pp. 89–91.

8. **724** HC Debs. col 510; 2nd Report from the Committee of Public Accounts, HC 158 of 1966–7, I, Qs 682 and 715; **737** HC Debs. col 93; editorials both 9 September 1966.

9. Third Report from the Committee of Public Accounts, HC 362 of 1968–9, Qs 4433–4 and 4463; *Economist*, 24 May 1969; but see also **773** HC Debs. col 278, and **776** HC Debs. col 108 (WAs).

10. **800** HC Debs. col 386; **805** HC Debs. cols 194–6, **817** HC Debs. col 138; 6th Report from the Expenditure Committee, 'Public Money in the Private Sector', HC 347 of 1971–2, report, paras. 75–91.

11. *Op. cit.*, HC 347 of 1971–2, Q 332.

12. For details see *op. cit.*, HC 265 1964–5, Qs 696–7, together with the C and AG's memo, Class IV, vote 7, paras 8, 12, 13; *op. cit.*, HC 158 of 1966–7, Qs 888–9; **737** HC Debs. col 99; 5th Report from the Committee of Public Accounts, HC 647 of 1966–7, Q 1527, Appendix 1, C and AG's memo, and report, para. 53; *op. cit.*, HC 312, Qs 4722–33;

13. Fifth Report from the Committee of Public Accounts, 1966–7, Part II, HC 647, C and AG's memo, paras 24–25, Qs 1632–6; *Financial Times*, 28 February 1968; *The Times*, 20 March 1968.

14. *Op. cit.*, HC 347 of 1971–2, report, para. 81.

15. *Op. cit.*, HC 265 of 1964–5, Qs 655–6; HC 647 of 1966–7, C and AG's memo, para. 9, Qs 1383–7, 1397–8, 1434, and report, para. 44.

16. *Op. cit.*, HC 265 of 1964–5, C and AG's memo, paras 24–25, Qs 673–4; HC 158 of 1966–7, Qs 795, 802, 889, 943.

17. C and AG's Civil Report (Classes I–V), paras 88, 92–101, 105; *op. cit.*, HC 362 of 1968–9, Qs 4720, 4561–3, 4568–70 and 4806–7; also *op. cit.*, HC 647 of 1966–7, C and AG's memo, para. 21 and Q 1569.

18. *Op. cit.*, HC 647 of 1966–7, C and AG's memo, paras 18–20, Qs 1581, 1546.

19. *Op. cit.*, HC 647 of 1966–7, Q 1565, 1555–9 and 1610. Also C and AG's memo, paras 18–20.

20. *Op. cit.*, HC 362 of 1968–9, Qs 4439 and 4473.

21. Downey Report, *op. cit.*, paras 285, 290–5, 312; *Report of the Committee on the Management and Control of Research and Development*, Office of the Minister for Science, 1961.

22. *Flight*, 18 November 1971, editorial.

23. *Aviation Week*, 4 September 1972, pp. 52–55 and p. 23.

24. **829** HC Debs. col 296; **846** HC Debs. col 154 (WAs).

25. *Op. cit.*, HC 148 of 1966–7, report, para. 27.

26. Brown, Neville, *New Scientist*, 13 July 1967.

27. *Op. cit.*, HC 42 of 1963–4, report, para. 85 and 7th Special

Report from the Estimates Committee, HC 241 of 1963-4, paras 7-10 (Treasury observations).

28. Statement by HMG, Prime Minister's Office, 26 October 1964, para. 13(6); **701** HC Debs. cols 503-15 and 77 (WA).

29. Keesings Contemporary Archives, 20399a, 1964.

30. **705** HC Debs. cols 197-202.

31. Treaty Series No. 3 (1963), Cmnd 1916, 1962.

32. See **848** HC Debs. cols 115-16. Also note at col 117 Mr Wedgwood Benn: 'In September 1968 we established criteria with the French, and dates by which they should be applied. We also outlined the procedures to be followed which, in effect, would free each Government to consider what action they should take either by agreeing to continue or by deciding not to do so. Since 1969 the Government, in effect, have had freedom of action restored to them for this purpose.'

And at col 183 Mr Cranley Onslow, Under-Secretary of State for Trade and Industry: 'I wonder whether it might not be that some of these criteria ceased to be effective conditions of the contract before his Government was defeated at the General Election in 1970.'

33. *Observer*, 25 April 1971 and *Sunday Times*, 2 March 1969 and 12 July 1970.

34. *Flight*, 27 May 1965, p. 814; **804** HC Debs. cols 555-8.

35. *Op. cit.*, HC 213 of 1968-9, Appendix 58.

36. Edwards, Sir George, 'U.K. Aerospace – A personal view', *Aeronautical Journal*, November 1972, pp. 633-40 at p. 639.

37. See for instance the stream of reports from the Council of Europe Committee on Science and Technology: Doc. 2279 (1967), Doc. 2446 (1968), Doc. 2639 (1969), Doc. 3068 (1972).

38. E.g. Council of Europe, Doc. 3072, January 1972, 'Report on the Economic Implications of the Introduction of Civil Supersonic Aircraft', Committee on Economic Affairs and Development; and Doc. 3071, January 1972, 'Report on Repercussions of Supersonic Civil Flights on Human and Natural Environment', Committee on Social and Health Questions.

39. *Op. cit.*, HC 362 of 1968-9, report, para. 42.

40. **776** HC Debs. col 1301.

41. **737** HC Debs. cols 38 and 97.

42. **791** HC Debs. col 1554, (Mr Frank Haley).

43. *Ibid.*, col 1535.

44. *Op. cit.*, HC 347 of 1971–2, report paras 75–91. Sir Robert Marshall is Secretary (Industry) at the DTI, Sir Samuel Goldman is Second Permanent Secretary at the Treasury.

45. *Ibid.*, para. 91.

46. But see 3rd Report from the Committee of Public Accounts, HC 447 of 1971–2, report, paras 27–35 (Jaguar).

47. Op cit., HC 141 of 1971–2, para. 6.

48. 18 November 1971, editorial; 2 March 1972, p. 340; 1 June 1972, editorial.

49. See also Donne, Michael, *Financial Times*, 3 August 1967.

50. Fifth Report from the Select Committee on Estimates, 'United Kingdom Atomic Energy Authority', HC 316 of 1958–9, para. 142 and Report from the Select Committee on Science and Technology, HC 381 xvii of 1966–7, para. 109.

51. Turpin, Colin, *Government Contracts*, (Harmondsworth: Penguin Books Ltd., 1972) pp. 264–5 and Edmonds, Martin, 'Government Contracting and Renegotiation: A Comparative Analysis', *50 Public Administration*, Spring 1972, pp. 45–64.

52. Consultative Assembly of the Council of Europe, Doc. 2893, *op. cit.*, p. 4; **737** HC Debs. cols 60 and 65, (Mr Edwin Brooks and Mr John Biffen); see also Simpson, John, 'The Political and Parliamentary Implications of Transnational Defence Procurement', in *Weapons Procurement, Defence Management and International Collaboration* (London: RUSI, 1972), pp. 29–35.

CHAPTER VII

1. Council of Europe, Third Parliamentary and Scientific Conference, Lausanne, 11–14 April 1972, PSC (72) Exp. II–1, Report on the second theme: European Science Policy, Professor Christopher Freeman.

2. Pavitt, K., 'Technology in Europe's Future', *1 Research Policy*, 3, July 1972, pp. 211–73.

3. Caused by 'the lack of political will and the slow machinery of intergovernmental cooperation' – Council of Europe, Doc. 3063, Report on European Scientific and Technological Cooperation', 17 December 1971, para. 32.

4. *Op. cit.*, HC 347 of 1971–2, Q 2491.

5. The highly charged debate in Britain in 1972–3 on the future of the aircraft has not been discussed here since it was relatively unconnected with the European dimension of the project, but see for instance Andrew Wilson's articles in the *Observer*, editorially supported, especially 23 April 1972; 7 May 1972; 21 and 28 January 1973; 4 February 1973. See also the reply by Mr Geoffrey Knight of BAC, *Observer*, 30 April 1972, and by Sir George Edwards of BAC, *The Times*, 9 February 1973 (letter).

6. See *Flight*, 28 December 1972, pp. 929–31.

7. See 'The DRAGON Project 1959–1969', *Atom*, No. 154, August 1969, and **300** HL Debs. cols 534–5, (Lord Sherfield). I am also grateful to Mr Kenneth Green for information on this subject, on which he has completed a doctoral thesis.

8. *Op. cit.*, HC 629 of 1970–71, Q 751.

9. *Ibid.*, SRC Memo. p. 141, para. 10 and Q 549.

10. *Ibid.*, Q 754.

11. Salomon, Jean-Jacques, 'European Scientific Organisations', in *Science and Technology in Europe*, Moonman, Eric, ed., *op. cit.*, pp. 63–86. Cf. Kowarski, L., *Bulletin of the Atomic Scientists*, December 1955, pp. 354–7.

12. Taylor, Paul, *International Cooperation Today: the European and the Universal Pattern* (London: Elek Books Ltd., 1971), quotation at p. 153; see also Russett, Bruce M., 'Transactions, Community and International Political Integration', 9 *Journal of Common Market Studies*, pp. 224–45, especially pp. 224–32.

13. Pinder, John, 'Problems of European Integration', in Denton, G. R., ed., *Economic Integration in Europe* (London: Weidenfeld and Nicolson, 1969), pp. 143–70, at pp. 145 and 163. Also 'Advanced Technology: Britain and the EEC', in Johnson, Harry G., *et al.*, *Economics: Britain and the EEC* (London: Longman, 1969), pp. 58–76.

14. Hansen, Roger, 'Regional Integration; reflections on a decade of theoretical efforts', *21 World Politics*, 2, 1969, reproduced in Hodges, Michael, *European Integration*, (Harmondsworth: Penguin Books, 1972), pp. 184–202.

15. But see also Wallace, Helen S., 'The Impact of the European Communities on National Policy Making', in Ionescu, Ghiṭa, ed., *The New Politics of European Integration*, (London: Macmillan, 1972), pp. 196–214 at p. 214.

16. Jantsch, Erich, *Technological Planning and Social Futures* (London: Cassel, 1972), pp. 177–8 and 181.

17. Lindberg, Leon N., *The Political Dynamics of European Economic Integration* (Stanford: Stanford U.P., 1963), pp. 44–45.

18. Lindberg, Leon N., and Scheingold, Stuart A., *Europe's Would-be Polity: Patterns of Change in the European Community* (Englewood Cliffs, N. J.: Prentice Hall Inc., 1970), p. 289.

19. Sewell, James Patrick, *Functionalism and World Politics*, (Princeton, N. J.: Princeton U.P., 1966), p. 3; note also Dawson, Raymond H. and Nicholson, George E. Jr., 'NATO and the SHAPE Technological Centre', *21 International Organisation*, 1967, pp. 545–91: 'The theory of functionalism in international organisation is grounded upon a set of assumptions about the impact of scientific and technological change and concomitant social change upon the nation state and the state system. It asserts that this process of change creates a spectrum of common problems or tasks which transcend "national" solution or control although they impinge directly upon the interests and welfare of the nation' (p. 566).

20. Sannwald, Rolf F., and Stohler, Jacques, *Economic Integration: Theoretical Assumptions and Consequences of European Integration* (Princeton, N. J.: Princeton U.P., 1959), p. 105.

21. Scitovsky, Tibor, *Economic Theory and Western European Integration* (London: Allen & Unwin, 1958), p. 149.

22. See *Interavia*, 1971, No. 11, p. 1219.

23. Wallich, Henry C., 'The United States and the European Economic Community: A Problem of Adjustment', *22 International Organisation*, 1968, pp. 841–54.

24. Nye, Joseph S., 'Comparative Regional Integration: Concept and Measurement', *ibid.*, pp. 855–880.

25. Kaiser, Karl, 'Transnational Politics: Toward a Theory of Multinational Politics', *25 International Organisation*, 1971, pp. 790–817.

26. Haas, Ernst B., 'The Study of Regional Integration', in Lindberg, Leon N., and Scheingold, Stuart A., eds., *Regional Integration Theory and Research* (Cambridge: Harvard U.P., 1971), reprinted from *24 International Organisation*, 4, Autumn 1970.

27. Schmitter, Philippe C., 'Central American Integration: Spill-over, Spill-around, or Encapsulation?' *9 Journal of Common*

Market Studies, pp. 1–48.

28. Belassa, Bela, *The Theory of Economic Integration* (London: Allen & Unwin, 1961), pp. 103–4 and 174–6.

29. Nau, Henry R., 'The Practice of Interdependence in the Research and Development Sector: Fast Reactor Cooperation in Western Europe', *26 International Organisation*, 3, Summer 1972, pp. 499–526.

30. Skolnikoff, Eugene B., 'Science and Technology: The Implications for International Institutions', *25 International Organisation*, 1971, pp. 759–75.

31. Wright, Christopher, 'Advanced Technologies and the Evolution of Europe in the 1970's: Lessons from the collapse of Rolls-Royce', in Warnecke, Steven Joshua, ed., *The European Community in the 1970's* (London: Praeger – Pall Mall Press, 1972), chapter 8, esp. pp. 151, 161 and 163.

32. See Haas, Ernst B., *The Uniting of Europe* (Stanford: Stanford U.P., 1958).

33. **221**, 22 February 1969, pp. 697–8.

34. Feld, Werner Joachim, *Transnational Business Collaboration Among Common Market Countries, its Implications for Political Integration* (New York: Praeger, 1970), pp. 97 and 121.

35. Quoted in Schwamm, Henri, 'The Significance of the new forms of industrial cooperation in Europe', *13 European Yearbook*, (The Hague: Martinus Nijhoff, 1967), 1965, pp. 60–72.

36. Franks, P. R., 'The Management Organisation of the Martel Project', *Aeronautical Journal*, January 1970, pp. 81–84.

37. Mr M. Heseltine in his first speech as Aerospace Minister, Rotary International, Long Eaton, Derbyshire, 7 May 1972, printed in *Flight*, 18 May 1972, pp. 725–6; Giusta, L., *op. cit.*; Heath, B. O., *op. cit.*

38. Piaganiol, Pierre, 'Scientific Policy and the European Community', *6 Minerva*, 3, Spring 1968, pp. 354–65; King, Alexander, 'Science and Technology in the New Europe', *Daedalus*, Winter 1964, pp. 434–58.

39. Ingrey, D. F., 'The Machinery of International Collaboration' and 'The Philosophy of International Equipment Collaboration', in *Weapons Procurement, Defence Management and International Collaboration (RUSI)*, *op. cit.*, pp. 20–29. *The Statement on the Defence Estimates 1973*, Cmnd 5231, states that 'Specialised sub-

groups of the Eurogroup [an informal group of Defence Ministers and NATO permanent representatives of ten European countries] have been set up to explore and promote closer European collaboration in arms procurement, logistics', etc. (chapter 1, paragraph 8). Four examples are given. Britain is already engaged in joint development projects with Belgium (combat reconnaissance vehicle) and with West Germany and Italy (versions of 155 mm howitzer), and in 1972 joined FINABEL, in which army chiefs-of-staff of West European countries meet to discuss harmonisation of tactics, logistics, etc.

40. Armand, Louis, and Drancourt, Michel, *The European Challenge* (London: Wiedenfeld and Nicolson, 1968), pp. 172, 221 and 248.

41. Maltzahn, D., 'Industrial Policy in the EEC', *4 Business Economist*, 2, June 1972, pp. 55–61, at p. 60, and Caty, G., 'Coordination of European Science and Technology', *1 Science Policy News*, 2, September 1969, p. 25–9.

42. Cf. Jacob, Philip E., and Teune, Henry, 'The Integration Process', in Jacob, Philip E., and Toscano, James V., *The Integration of Political Communities* (New York: J. B. Lippincott, 1964), pp. 30 and 35.

43. *National Science Policies in Europe*, Unesco, Science Policy Studies and Documents, No. 17, 1970, report, para. 91, p. 53.

CHAPTER VIII

1. Though it must be admitted, for example, that before the UK bought a third share, for £10 millions, of the Franco-West German high flux reactor at Grenoble, the Government had previously turned down an SRC request for £22 millions for a similar, wholly British, proposal – *239 Nature*, p. 60, 1972 and **241**, p. 6, 1973. Sir Brian Flowers, SRC chairman, in a lecture at Newcastle University, 15 March 1973, stated: 'International projects can be expected to run into difficulties because of the complexities of multigovernmental decision-making . . . but difficulties also arise nationally when responsibilities straddle more than one Department of Government. When both considerations occur simultaneously matters can be difficult indeed. My next story, which deals with the provision of high flux neutron beams for UK

scientists, illustrates this.' (p. 8). This lecture also deals with the 300 Gev accelerator.

2. Bondi, Hermann, 'International Collaboration in Advanced Technology', *World Today*, January 1973, pp. 16–23 (abridged text of 21st Stevenson Memorial Lecture at The London School of Economics, 22 November 1972).

3. *The Times*, 5 March 1969.

4. *New Scientist*, 18 February 1971, pp. 348–9.

5. An argument put forward, for instance, in Layton, Christopher, Hu, Y. S., and Whitehead, Michael, *Industry and Europe* (London: PEP Broadsheet, No. 531, 1971), p. 83.

6. Of interest here is de Hoghton, Charles, *Cross Channel Collaboration: a Study of Agreements between British and Continental Firms* (London: PEP, 1967).

7. Bourguignon, *op. cit.*, says that an *à la carte* approach 'can only result in a dissipation of efforts which is prejudicial to the formation of big enough markets and structures and prejudicial to the satisfactory administration of public resources'. The approach favoured here is instead along the lines set down in the conclusion to Buchan, Alastair, ed., *Europe's Futures, Europe's Choices* (London: Chatto & Windus, for the Institute for Strategic Studies, 1969). This refers to a 'mixed, functional Europe', 'partly inter-governmental, partly supranational', 'flexible and open', and it adds that there 'might be a limited Defence Community and a Techno-logical Community, both with supranational characteristics but depending on the degree of common interest that could be mobil-ized' (pp. 162–6).

8. See, for instance, two recent calls: Kenward, Michael, 'Accountability in high technology', *New Scientist*, 22 February 1973, pp. 425–6 and Corina, Maurice, 'Technology projects need tighter control', *The Times*, 6 February 1973.

9. *Op. cit.*, Project Perseus, para. 82.

10. Adams, J. B., 'CERN: The European Organisation for Nuclear Research', in Cockroft, Sir John, ed., *The Organisation of Research Establishments* (Cambridge: The University Press, 1965), Chapter 14, at p. 244.

11. Note 'International collaboration . . . does not in itself solve the problems of economical project selection or of a cost conscious-ness in project execution. Indeed it may accentuate both problems'

Peck, Merton J., 'Science and Technology', in Caves, Richard E., and associates, *Britain's Economic Prospects*, for The Brookings Institution, (London: Allen & Unwin, 1968), pp. 448–84 at p. 475. Note also the following comment on the Research and Development Society's 1973 conference on European cooperation: The lessons seem to be both political and industrial. Long-term objectives should be established, and the political aims should be compatible with the programme. Work-sharing arrangements should include provisions for parity changes, and should reflect the respective levels of technology as well as financial contributions. Concorde-type committee structures are not advisable; the programme should be run by one man. Industry should have clear financial incentives; multi-national contracting should be avoided. Industrial arrangements should ensure a competitive situation for the customer. And, ideally, the industrial partners should be about equal in their capabilities. (*The Times*, 9 April 1973).

12. See interview with Herr Brandt, *The Times*, 27 February 1973.

13. Gilpin, *France in the Age of the Scientific State*, *op. cit.*

14. This does not offend the spirit of Andrew Shonfield's Reith Lectures of 1972: 'Journey to an Unknown Destination,' *Listener*, 9 November to 14 December 1972.

15. Wild, Rolf H., 'Development Cost and Profit', *Interavia*, 1972, No. 3, pp. 198–9.

16. *The Conditions for Success in Technological Innovation* (Paris: OECD, 1971), para. 243.

17. Bellamy, Ian, 'Defence Procurement – A Heretical View', *RUSI Journal*, March 1972, pp. 37–9.

18. Pickles, William, 'Political Hopes and Political Realities', in Evans, Douglas, ed., *Destiny or Delusion: Britain and the Common Market*, (London: Gollancz, 1971), pp. 109–20 at p. 120.

Principal abbreviations used in the text

AEA	Atomic Energy Authority
AFVG	Anglo-French Variable Geometry Aircraft
AGR	Advanced Gas-cooled Reactor
AICMA	Association Internationale des Constructeurs de Matériel Aérospatial
BAC	British Aircraft Corporation
AWR	Boiling Water Reactor
CBI	Confederation of British Industry
CEA	Commissariat à l'Énergie Atomique
CEGB	Central Electrictiy Generating Board
CERD	Committee for European Research and Development
CERN	European Centre for Nuclear Research
DEA	Department of Economic Affairs
DTI	Department of Trade and Industry
ECSC	European Coal and Steel Community
ELDO	European Launcher Development Organisation
EMBO	European Molecular Biology Organisation
ENEA	European Nuclear Energy Agency
ERDA	European Research and Development Agency
ESRO	European Space Research Organisation
ESC	European Space Conference
GIE	Groupement d'Intérêt Économique
IAEA	International Atomic Energy Agency
ICL	International Computers Limited
IEA	Industrial Expansion Act
IRC	Industrial Reorganisation Corporation
MRCA	Multi-role Combat Aircraft
NRDC	National Research Development Corporation
PWR	Pressurised Water Reactor
R & D	Research and Development
SALT	Strategic Arms Limitation Talks
VG	Variable Geometry

Name Index

Abs, Hermann Josef, 175n
Adams, J. B., 203n
Adams, Walter, 176n
Aigrain, Pierre, 45
Albonetti, Achille, 80, 84
Armand, Louis, 32, 150
Ashcroft, Geoffrey, 193n

Bambridge, Anthony, 49
Barnaby, C. F., 189n
Barzel, Rainer, 88
Basiuk, Victor, 32–3
Beaton, Leonard, 85–6, 120, 155
Beck, Robert H., 178n
Beddington-Behrens, Sir Ed., 31
Beesley, M. E., 173n
Behrman, Jack N., 179n
Belassa, Bela, 144, 147
Bellamy, Ian, 166
Beloff, Nora, 15
Ben-David, Joseph, 176n
Berschin, H. Hervert, 179n
Beteille, R., 70
Biffen, John, 198n
Blackall, T. E., 184n
Blackett, Professor, 16
Boffey, Philip, 178n
Bondi, Professor, 78, 100, 140, 152
Bourgiugnon, Pierre, 181n, 203n
Bradley, F. H., 56
Brandt, Herr, 77, 204n
Bray, Jeremy, 172n
Brenner, Michael J., 189n
Brittan, Samuel, 15
Broadway, Frank, 172n
Brooke, Michael Z., 179n
Brooks, Edwin, 198n
Brooks, Harvey, 178n
Brown, Neville, 127
Brown, Sir Stanely, 82
Buchan, Alastair, 203n
Burrows, Sir Bernard, 195n

Cairns, David, 75
Calmann, John, 31

Carrington, Lord, 189n
Casimir, Professor, 27, 183n
Caty, Gilbert, 180n, 202n
Chataway, C., 11, 12, 55, 91, 183n
Châtenet, M., 40
Chesterton, G. K., 56
Clarke, Sir Richard, 172n
Cobham, Michael J., 194n
Colonna, G., 182n, 183n
Corfield, F., 67, 73, 89–90, 111, 114, 181n
Corina, Michael, 203n
Costello, John, 184n
Cousins, Frank, 17
Crane, Diana, 112–13

Davies, John, 10, 11, 12, 13, 14–15, 59
Davis, John, 184n
Dawson, Raymond H., 200n
Debré, M., 87, 189n
de Gaulle, General, 22, 37, 79
Deghand, James L., 187n
de Hoghton, Charles, 184n, 293n
Dè la Machotière, Stuart, 190n
Deutsch, K., 143, 149
Diebold, John, 25
Donne, Michael, 198n
Downey, W. E., 194n
Drancourt, Michel, 150
Duchêne, François, 88
Dunning, John H., 23, 179n
Düren, Albrecht, 47, 179n

Edmonds, M., 136, 185n
Edwards, Sir George, 109, 116, 130, 199n
Elgin, Roger, 173n, 186n
Elstub, St John, 185n
Epstein, Barbara, 81
Etzioni, A., 143
Evans, L. G., 193n
Ezra, Derek, 184n

Faith, Nicholas, 34, 173n
Fanfani, Signor, 22

Feld, Werner Joachim, 148–9
Flowers, Sir Brian, 203n
Foch, René, 31
Foix, François, 182n
Franks, P. R., 184n, 192n, 201n
Freeman, Professor, 138

Galbraith, J. K., 159
Geddes, Sir Reay, 50
Gee, Jack, 184n
Gilpin, Robert, 27, 163
Giusta, L., 192n, 201n
Goldman, Sir Samuel, 134, 198n
Graham, Andrew, 172n
Green, Kenneth, 199n
Greenberg, Daniel S., 34
Greenhalgh, G. H., 193n
Greenwood, A. H. C., 192n, 193n
Gregory, Frank, 58–9, 191n
Grierson, Ronald, 177n
Gueron, J., 180n

Haas, E., 143, 144, 147, 201n
Häfele, W., 193n
Hansen, Roger, 144
Harlow, Christopher, 184n
Harman, Alvin J., 190n
Healey, D., 62, 81
Heath, B. O., 185n, 201n
Heath, E., 55, 86, 108
Herodotus, 71
Heseltine, M., 135, 201n
Hill, Walter, 115
Hirsch, M., 40
Holloman, J. Herbert, 26
Hornig, Donald, 26
Hotz, R., 99
Hu, Y. S., 203n
Hughes, Terry, 184n

Ingrey, D. F., 150
Irwin, Christopher, 195n
Iserland, K., 192n

Jacob, Philip E., 202n
James, Robert Rhodes, 185n
Jantsch, Erich, 145
Jenkins, Roy, 128, 185n
Jenkins, W. B., 99
Jewkes, Professor, 16
Johnson, President, 26
Johnson, Timothy, 173n

Joseph, Sir Keith, 9, 13
Joucla, Gérard, 69, 110–11

Kaiser, Karl, 147
Keegan, Victor, 174n
Kenrick, K. G., 191n
Kenward, Michael, 203n
Kindleberger, Charles P., 179n
King, Alexander, 149
Knapp, John, 177n
Knight, Geoffrey, 199n
Knoppers, Antonie, 177n
Kowarski, L., 199n
Kraijenhoff, G., 180n

Layton, Christopher, 30–1, 69, 94–5,
    181n, 183n, 184n, 203n
Leslie, S. C., 177n
Levitt, Theodore, 25
Lindberg, Leon N., 200

McClelland, W. G., 173n, 177n
Macioti, Manfredo, 176n
McKnight, Allan, 189n
McLachlan, D. L., 24
McNamara, Robert, 25, 139
Mallaleiu, J. W. P., 186n
Maltzahn, D., 202n
Mann, F. A., 47
Maréchal, André, 45
Marshall, Sir Robert, 133, 198n
Messmer, M., 189n
Metternich, 138
Meyer, Sir Anthony, 32
Miles, Caroline M., 179
Miller, Linda B., 172n
Monnet, Jean, 31
Moonman, Eric, 32

Nau, Henry R., 33, 147
Nicholson, George E., 200n
Nieburg, H. L., 40
Nouille, J., 192n
Nye, Joseph S., 146

Onslow, Cranley, 197n
Owen, David, 86

Park, Ford, 23
Part, Sir Anthony, 172n
Pavitt, K., 138, 178n
Peck, Merton J., 204n

Pfaltzgraff, Robert L., 176n, 187n
Pickles, William, 204n
Pierre, Andrew J., 87
Piganiol, Pierre, 149
Pinder, John, 143
Plowden, William, 172n, 173
Polach, Jaroslav G., 39
Pompidou, M., 77, 128

Quinn, J. B., 23

Ramsden, J. M., 185n
Rayner, D. G., 191n
Redeker, J. A., 189n
Reed, Arthur, 184n
Reed, Laurence, 32
Remmers, H. Lee, 179n
Rhodes, J. B., 178n
Richardson, Jacques, 23
Ridley, Nicholas, 10
Rippon, Geoffrey, 59, 192n
Russett, Bruce M., 199n

Salomon, Jean-Jacques, 141–2
Sanders, Professor, 47
Sannwald, Rolf F., 146
Schaerf, T. F., 33
Scheingold, Stuart A., 145
Scheinman, Lawrence, 180n
Schmitter, Philippe C., 144, 147
Schmitthoff, Professor Clive, 182n
Schumann, Maurice, 79
Schwamm, Henri, 210n
Scitovsky, Tibor, 146
Servan-Schreiber, J. J., 22, 23
Sewell, James Patrick, 145
Sherfield, Lord, 81, 199n
Siekman, Philip, 182n
Silver, C. C., 51–2
Simpson, John, 58–9, 191n, 198n
Skolnikoff, Eugene B., 148
Smart, Ian, 189n
Smith, A. H., 193n
Spannier, David, 175n
Spence, Daniel Lloyd, 28
Spinelli, Altiero, 177n
Stephenson, Hugh, 37

Steuer, M. D., 175n
Stohler, Jacques, 146
Suranyi-Unger, Theodore, 175n
Swann, D., 24

Taylor, Paul, 142–3
Thompson, Dennis, 47
Thomson, George, 87
Toscano, James V., 202n
Toulemon, R., 183n
Tugendhat, Christopher, 49, 179n
Turner, Louis, 36
Turpin, Colin, 136

Valentine, Burl, 187n
Van Dijck, J. M., 180n
Vasseur, Michel, 182n
Vellas, Pierre, 176n
Villiers, Charles, 29
Vernon, Raymond, 179n
Vig, Norman J., 172n

Wallace, Helen S., 199n
Wallich, Henry C., 146
Waltz, Kenneth, 179n
Warner, Malcolm, 180n
Warren, Kenneth, 193n
Watson, Alan, 172n
Wedgwood Benn, Anthony, 10, 11, 13, 59, 66, 74, 84, 132, 155, 179, 197n
White, C. B., 191n
White, G. M., 173n
Whitehead, Michael, 191n, 203n
Wiggs, Richard, 184n
Wild, Rolf H., 165
Williams, B. R., 175n
Wilshere, David, 34
Wilson, Andrew, 199n
Wilson, H., 21, 22, 23, 29, 33
Wilson, James A., 176n
Winning, Anthony, 180n
Wood, David, 15
Wright, Christopher, 148

Young, Stephen, 173n

Ziegler, Henri, 96, 116, 191n

Subject Index

À la carte approach, 32, 41, 43, 57, 74, 203n
Accountability, 9–12, 130–7, 158–64, 203n
Action Committee for a United States of Europe, 31
AEG, 83, 88, 89
Aeritalia, 98
Aeroengines, 8, 18, 67–8, 70
Aérospatiale, 96, 97, 141
Agfa-Gevaert, 49
Agip Nucleare, 12
Aigrain plan, 45, 52, 89, 91
Air League, 66
Airborne early warning aircraft (AEW), 59
Airbus, European, 63–4, 69, 95, 96–7, 110, 139, 146
Aircraft industry, 8, 18, 19, 59–70, 146
Airlines, 63, 64, 68, 154
Alpha Jet, 61, 98
American Challenge, The, 22
American industry, 21, 23–6, 28, 30, 34, 35, 46, 51, 79, 81, 82, 88–90, 91, 108, 109, 153, 167, 168
Anglo-French Variable Geometry Aircraft (AFVG), 59–60, 64, 110, 111, 129
APC, 79
ASEA-Atom, 82
Association Internationale des Construteurs de Matériel Aérospatial (AICMA), 68, 69
Atlantique, 60, 61, 95–6, 124, 126
Atomic Energy Authority (AEA), 8, 17, 40, 43, 79, 81, 136
Austria, 45
Aviation Week, 99
Avionica, 98, 108
Avionics, 8, 70, 108–10

Belgium, 62, 66, 69, 71, 81, 85, 111
Belgonucleare, 79, 81, 82
Black Arrow, 112, 174n
Blue Streak, 71, 72, 73, 111, 174n

BNFL, 82
Board of Trade, 8
Brain drain, 26, 176n
Breguet, 61, 69, 95–6
Bristol Siddeley, 18
British Aircraft Corporation (BAC), 18, 63, 69, 74, 98, 120–2, 174n
British Association, 26
Brown Boverie, 79, 82
Burroughs, 91

Canada, 61, 62
Caravelle, 60
CASA, 96
Causse Committee, 72
CDC, 89
CEA, 40, 79
CENTEC, 104
CERN (European Organisation for Nuclear Research), 2, 57, 64, 67, 71, 92–3, 112–13, 139, 141–2, 144, 157, 160, 203n
CETS (European Conference on Communications Satellites), 102
Channel Tunnel, 57, 92–3
CII, 89, 90
CITEC, 89
Citroen, 57
Civil Service, 6, 110–11, 135
Collaboration (distinguished from co-operation), 3–4, 162–3
Colonna plan, 48–9, 55
Commission of the EEC, 29, 31, 41, 50, 70, 80, 85, 91–2, 139, 146, 168–70
  industrial policy, 47–9, 55, 156
  technology policy, 43–6, 53–5, 156
Commitment (to collaborate), 5, 57–93, 152–9
Company law, 21, 44
Computer industry, 8, 17, 18, 88–92, 190n
Concorde, 2, 7, 18, 63, 64, 135, 139, 146, 147, 149, 167, 184n, 199n
  commitment, 59, 66, 67, 197n

Concorde—*contd.*
costs, 115, 117–23, 126
equity, 104–6, 110
organisation, 95, 97
parliamentary control, 131–4, 161
withdrawal provisions, 127–8
Confederation of British Industry (CBI), 11, 21, 28, 191n
Conservative government, 6, 8, 12, 17, 18, 55, 63, 64, 69, 121
Conservative party conference, 13, 86
Control (of collaboration), 4, 115–37, 158–61
Cost control, 117–27, 203n
COST group, 46, 53
Cost of collaboration, 115–16
Council of Europe, Science and Technology Committee, 131
Council of the EEC, 29, 44, 45, 158
Criteria of evaluation, 138–42

Daf, 57
Dassault, 60, 61, 69, 98–9
Defence, technology and, 5, 16, 31, 32, 58–9, 141, 149–50
Department of Economic Affairs, 8, 9
Department of Scientific and Industrial Research (DSIR), 8
Department of Trade and Industry (DTI), 7, 8, 9, 51, 133–4
Disengagement, 6, 13
Dornier, 65, 98
Downey Report, 111, 123, 124
DRAGON, 67, 81, 82, 103, 113, 136, 140, 147, 199n
Dunlop-Pirelli, 50, 182n

Economic planning, 6
Economist, 1, 7, 20, 24, 26, 79, 119
EDF, 79
Efficiency in collaboration, 4, 104–14, 158–9
Electricity utilities, 82, 154
Electronic Engineering Association, 109
Electronics International, 34
Elliott Automation, 108, 109, 174n
Elstub Report, 65
Engins Matra, 97
English Electric, 17, 89
Enrichment facilities, 41, 84–6
Estimates Committee, Select Committee on, 71, 112, 125, 127, 131, 136
Euratom, 39–43, 80, 81, 103, 139, 145, 157, 158
Euro HKG, 82
Eurochemic, 84, 103
Eurodata consortium, 89
Europe Tomorrow, 30
European Advanced Technology: A Programme for Integration, 30
European Armaments Agency, 31–2, 150
European Coal and Steel Community (ECSC), 43
European Communities: British membership of, 1, 22, 28, 51–3, 55–6, 167
European companies, 21, 47, 49–50, 96
European Defence Community, 39, 203n
European Investment Bank, 49, 54
European Launcher Development Organisation (ELDO), 66, 70–3, 75, 77, 78, 95, 100–2, 111–13, 139, 141
European Molecular Biology Organisation (EMBO), 113
European Nuclear Energy Agency (ENEA), 40, 80, 81, 84, 102–3, 136
European Organisation for Civil Aviation Electronics (EURO-CAE), 68
European Parliament, 31, 131, 161
European Political Community, 39
European R & D Agency (ERDA), 46
European R.&D. Committee (CERD), 31, 46, 54, 183n
European Science Foundation, 30, 54
European Space Agency, 102
European Space Conference (ESC), 73, 75, 102
European Space Research Organisation (ESRO), 70, 71, 77–8, 89, 91, 100–2, 111–13, 126, 140–1, 152–3, 157
European Weather Centre, 52
Europlane, 65
EUROSPACE, 74
Evaluation of collaboration, 4, 138–42, 161–4

Expenditure Committee, Select Committee on, 62, 119, 121, 125, 131, 133
F104, 69
Fiat, 57, 67
Fiat G91, 61
Financial Times, 34, 119
Finland, 46
Flight International, 110, 135
Fokker 28 Fellowship, 66, 98
FORATOM, 102–3
Fortune, 34
France, 19, 27, 36, 37, 47, 50, 57, 71, 72, 77, 80, 81, 82, 96, 111, 113, 123, 135, 141, 163
and Britain, 22, 45, 59, 60, 62, 68, 75–6, 78–9, 83, 85, 86–7, 89, 91, 92, 97–8, 105–7, 110–11, 117–18, 120, 121, 122, 127–8, 132, 133
and Euratom, 39, 40, 42, 43

Gas Breeder Reactor Association, 82
General Election, 6, 26, 89
General Electric (USA), 63, 68, 79, 82, 83, 89
GGA, 82
GHN, 81
Gibb-Zuckerman Report, 123
Greece, 46
Groupement d'intérêt économique (GIE), 48, 96
Guardian, 34, 119

Halden research reactor, 103
Hawker Siddeley, 18, 64, 65, 66, 69, 96, 174n
Helicopters (Anglo-French package), 59, 97, 106, 110, 149
Honeywell, 89
HS 1182, 66, 67

IBM, 88, 90
Imperatives of technology, 7, 20, 156
Industrial Development Executive, 11
Industrial Expansion Act 1968, 7, 10, 12
Industrial policy (EEC), 46–51
Industrial Reorganisation Corporation (IRC), 7, 8, 9, 10, 12, 17, 19, 29, 30, 49, 173n
Industrial restructuring, 7
Industry Act, 10, 12, 13, 14, 15

Infiltrators, The, 34
Institute of Technology, 21, 33–4, 47, 113
Integration, 1–2, 39, 142–51, 162–3, 170, 200n
Intelstat, 73–4, 102
Inter Nuclear, 81–2
Interatom, 81, 82, 83
Interavia, 97
International Atomic Energy Agency (IAEA), 42, 180n
International Civil Aviation Organisation (ICAO), 68
International Computers Limited (ICL), 17, 18, 19, 89, 90, 91
Interventionism, 6, 7, 13, 14, 15, 17, 19, 167
Intramural costs of Concorde, 105–6
Ispra, 52
Italy, 20, 60, 61, 62, 69, 71, 78, 80, 85, 107, 113, 124–5

Jaguar, 18, 59, 60, 62, 64, 67, 95, 97, 98, 106, 109, 110, 124, 129, 134
Japan, 30, 51, 91, 168
Jeumont Schneider, 79
Juste retour, 40, 104–14, 142, 153, 195n

KHD, 67
KWU, 81, 82–3

Labour Government, 5–6, 7, 12, 13, 16, 17, 21, 59, 63, 64, 121, 127–8
'Lame duck' policy, 13
Lefevre Mission, 73
Lockheed, 18, 63, 64, 68, 161

Machine tools, 8
Machines Bull, 89
MAN, 57
Management of projects, 94–104
Marshall Report, 69
Martel, 59, 97, 98, 107, 149
MBB, 65, 96, 98
Medium Term Economic Committee, 44, 50
Memorandum of Understanding, 123, 124, 129, 154
Mercure, 98
Mergers, 47–9
Ministry of Aviation, 8, 105
Ministry of Aviation Supply, 8
Ministry of Defence, 115, 129, 134

Ministry of Power, 8
Ministry of Technology, 7, 8, 9, 17, 62, 121, 155, 172n
Mirage, 60, 61, 69
Motor Vehicles, 8, 19, 156
MTU, 67, 98
Multinational companies, 34–8, 156–7, 179n
Multi-role combat aircraft (MRCA), 60–1, 64, 67, 146, 149
commitment, 62, 107
costs, 124–5
equity, 108, 109
organisation, 95, 97, 98
parliamentary control, 134, 135
withdrawal provisions, 129

National Board for Prices and Incomes NBPI), 9
National Industrial Space Committee (NISC), 74
National Research Development Corporation (NRDC), 7, 8, 30
National Sovereignty, 1, 138, 147
NATO, 61, 69, 86, 114
Nature, 148, 183n
Neratoom, 81, 82
Netherlands, 43, 62, 64, 69, 71, 80, 81, 84–6, 113
Nixdorf, 90
Non-proliferation treaty, 42, 180n
Nuclear fuel, 83–6, 103, 104
Nuclear industry, 16–17, 19, 78–86, 174n
Nuclear weapons, 76, 85–8, 144, 152, 170, 189n

Observer, 26
Olivetti, 89
Organisation of projects, 94–104, 151, 158–9, 191n
Orgel reactor, 40

Panavia, 98, 124, 158
Paris summit, 53, 55–6, 75
Patents, 21, 44, 113
Philips, 89, 90, 91
Pierrelatte, 85
Plan Calcul, 89
Plowden Report, 61, 65, 69, 146, 167
Plowden-Winnacker Report, 31
Portugal, 45

Post-Apollo programme, 73, 75, 78
PREST group, 45, 53, 181n
Process of collaboration, 4, 94–114, 158–9
Procurement Executive, 8, 111
Public Accounts Committee, 63, 105–6, 120, 121, 131–3, 136

RB-211, 7, 18, 63, 67, 125, 161, 167, 168
Reactors, nuclear, 17, 40, 78–83, 103, 104, 147–8, 167
Regional Development Fund, 55
Rolls Royce, 18, 19, 64, 66, 67, 95, 97, 98, 107, 121, 125
Rothschild Report, 16
Royal Society, 26

Saab, 65
SABCA, 69
SALT talks, 33, 170
SAVIEM, 57
Science and Technology Act 1965, 7, 112
Science and Technology, Select Committee on, 9, 74, 89, 136
Science (European), 149, 152, 202n
Science Policy Research Unit (SPRU), 138, 139, 160
Science Research Council (SRC), 141
SEPECAT, 97, 98
SFU, 83
Shipbuilding Industry Board (SIB), 7, 9
Short Brothers and Harland, 66
Siemens, 83, 89, 90, 91
SKF, 29
SNAM-Progetti, 79, 81
Snecma, 66, 67, 68
SOCIA, 79
Society of British Aerospace Companies, 109
South Africa, 61
Space industry (British), 174n
Spain, 45, 81
Spey-Mirage, 60
Statement on the Defence Estimates, 62, 201n
Sweden, 3, 29, 36, 45, 80, 113, 164
Switzerland, 45
Symphonie, 77, 102, 141

Technical change as source of political problems, 3, 165

Technological community, 21, 28, 32, 203n

Technology gap, 3, 16, 145–6, 176n, 177n, 179n

Technology policy, British, 5–19, 51–3, 55, 167–8

Tihange, 81

The Times, 14, 22, 92–3, 107, 204n

TNPG, 79, 81, 82–3

Transall, 60, 95–6

Tripartite project, 84–6, 102, 146

TUC, 21, 38

Turboméca, 66, 67, 97

Turbo-Union, 98, 107

Turkey, 46

United Kingdom Council of the European Movement, 31

United Reprocessors, 83

United States, 22, 26, 27, 31, 32, 33, 36, 40, 61, 68, 73, 75, 76, 77, 78, 86, 87, 146, 161, 163

UNIVAC, 91

URENCO, 104

VFW-Fokker, 49, 65, 69, 95, 96, 125

VFW-Fokker 614, 66, 98–9

Vinter Report, 83

Volvo, 57, 67

West Germany, 19, 27, 44, 60, 62, 66, 69, 71, 77, 78, 80, 81, 82, 83, 84–6, 87, 89, 96, 107, 108, 113, 124, 125, 129, 141

Western European Union, Committee on Scientific, Technological and Aerospace Questions, 131

Westinghouse, 79, 81, 82, 83, 84, 89

Westland, 97, 106, 174n

Withdrawal provisions, 127–30, 157

Yugoslavia, 46